Face-to-Face with Doug Schoon
Volume II

Science and facts about nails/nail products for the educationally inclined.

Volume 2 contains fact-based answers to questions from actual nail professionals regarding natural nail anatomy, services and salons.

Based on "Face to Face with Doug Schoon", Episodes 1-50

The information in this book has been updated from the video series and contains significant amounts of new or recently discovered information, as well as, many special topics not found in the video series.

Many images in the book are shown also in 3D.

View these images use Red/Cyan Anaglyph 3D glasses

Ordering information can be found in the Appendix

ISBN: 978-0-9979186-2-5
Library of Congress Control Number: 2016916821

An updated, adaption of the scripts of:

"Face-to-Face with Doug Schoon"

Episodes 1-50

Volume 2

1st Edition

Categories
(Continued from volume 1)

Episode#: Question#

Natural Nail Structure

2: Myth - Taking a prenatal vitamin during pregnancy makes your nails grow faster?

Some claim that, “Prenatal vitamins are why women’s nails grow like crazy!” This is not correct. With or without prenatal vitamins, pregnant women’s nail growth accelerates, with the highest recorded rate during the last month of pregnancy. After delivery growth rates almost immediately return to normal- even if prenatal vitamins are taken. This is most likely due to the surge of growth hormones in the body during pregnancy. Vitamins can’t make your nails grow faster than just eating healthy. If you don’t eat healthy, vitamins certainly won’t make your nails grow any faster. Save your money and use high quality nail oil. You’ll be much better off.

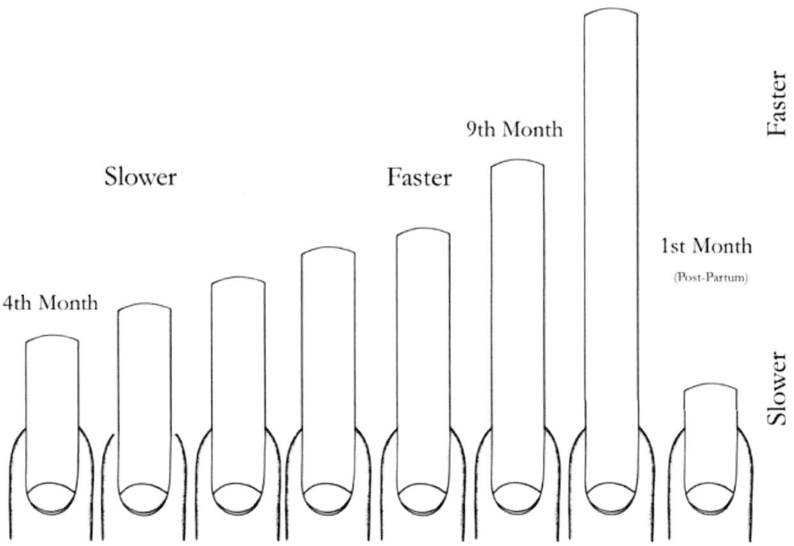

Image 1: Natural nail plate growth rates during pregnancy.

13:5 Can you explain a bit more about the nail breathing and the cuticle area breathing? I told a nail student once that the nail doesn't breathe so you don't need to give your nails a rest from any nail coatings and she said "but the cuticle breathes"?

I'm assuming your student doesn't understand what the cuticle is, or they would not have made this erroneous statement. Cuticle is dead tissue on the nail plate and therefore has no need nor does it have any capability for breathing. More than likely, this student was actually referring to the living skin at the base of the nail plate which is properly called the "eponychium" and proximal nail fold not the cuticle. This helps demonstrate why using the correct terminology is so important and why you as an educator should understand and insist that the correct terminology is used. If you understood these terms properly, you could have quickly replied that the cuticle doesn't need to breathe either; it's a thin layer of dead, colorless tissue that serves as a seal between the living skin and the nail plate that can't breathe and never needs to breathe.

The cuticle is removed before any nail coating is applied, breathing is not an option.

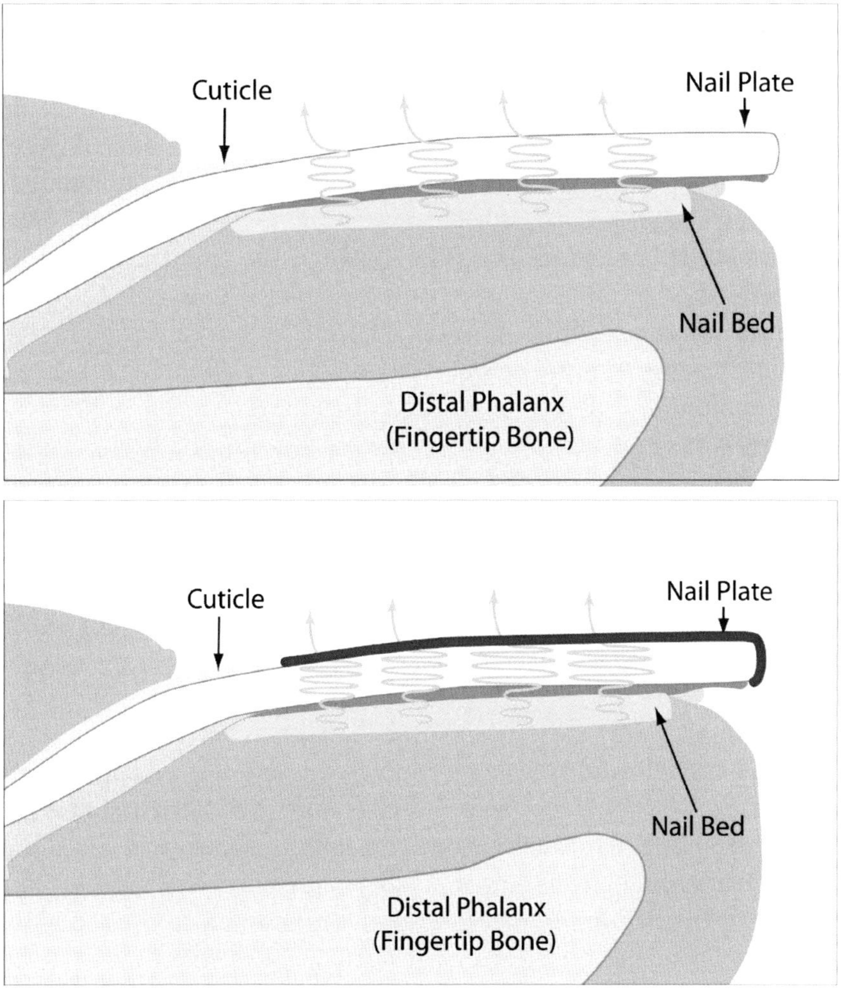

Image 2 and 3: Moisture transmission thought the nail, with and without nail polish.

Special Topic - One common reason for why nail polish can quickly peel from the nail plate.

The first image demonstrates how water moves though the nail plate. The nail plate allows for high rates of transmission of water molecules. Water (aka moisture) migrates quickly though the plate, but as shown, the molecules don't travel a straight line. Instead water molecules meander through the tiny (microscopic) channels that riddle the inside of a nail plate. This results in the plate containing about 15% water content, for a normal nail. Nail polish can slow the movement of water, but it doesn't completely stop its slow and steady migration toward the surface. Image 3 demonstrates how nail polish can slow this migration and raise the moisture content of the nail plate. The increased amount of water in the plate increases the water pressure inside the plate. As water pressure builds up underneath nail polish, it creates a force which can push upward on the underside of the nail polish and cause it to peel away from the surface. Even though water flow is relatively slow, the pressures which build up can become significant.

Here's an easy way to visualize this. Imagine a water hose that is trickling very slowly. Holding a thumb over the nozzle will initially block the flow, but this also causes water pressure to increase inside the hose. Eventually, the increased pressure will force the water inside the hose to squirt out between the thumb and nozzle. This happens inside the nail plate and the buildup in pressure can push or lift the nail polish from the surface to cause it to peel.

Image 4 (below): Shows a typical passage way inside the nail plate that allows the movement of water molecules. Other separate passages allow oils to move through the nail plate, as well. However, it is expected there are more water passages than oil passages, since larger amounts of water move through the plate at much faster rates than do natural oils. This passageway inside the nail plate is created at a junction where three nail cells meet, but don't fit together perfectly, however other types exist, e.g. small spaces between two cells. Such passages allow water molecules to migrate through the nail plate. The width of this image is about one-fifth the diameter of a human hair.

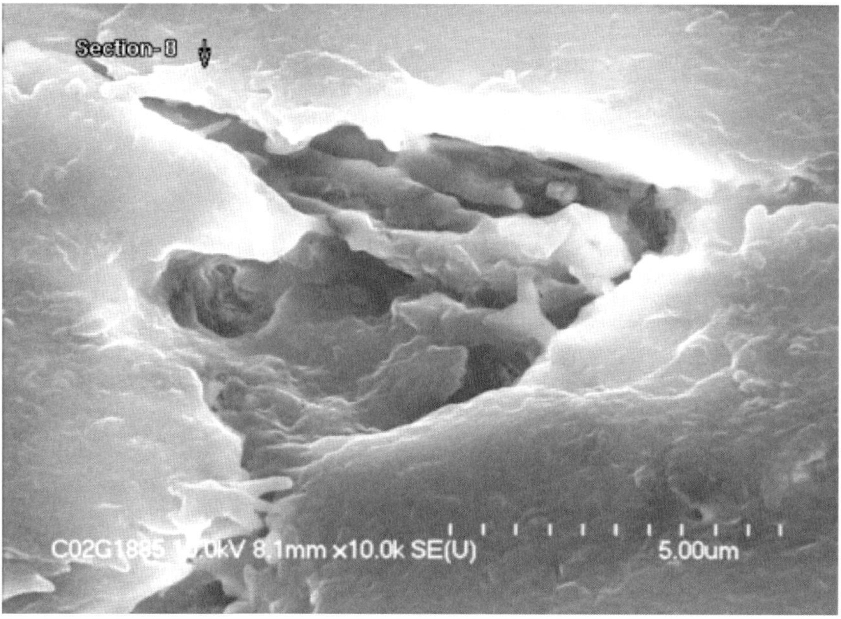

Image 4: Microscopic passageway inside the nail plate.

14:2 My teacher told me that if I soak the nails too long in water, this will dry them out. That doesn't make sense to me, so I thought I would ask if this is true.

It is a very common misunderstanding that soaking the nails dries them out. How can soaking the nails in water make them dry? That makes no sense. Water cannot cause anything to become dry. Extra water inside the nail plate causes it to become wetter. If the extra water leaves, the nail plate returns to its normal levels of moisture. The plate always contains some moisture, which is the same as saying it contains water. I think what your teacher was trying to say is that excessive water exposure can damage some nail plates when they are repeatedly exposed to water and then dried out again.

Excessive water exposure can be damaging to the plate, e.g. causing tiny cracks to rapidly grow into larger ones; or the plate to peel more at the free-edge. This damage is sometimes confused with dryness, even though they are not the same. The nail plate likely has the same water content as it did before, but now the surface damage has become more visible. How does water cause this damage to occur? When nails contain their normal levels of moisture, around 15%, they won't easily bend, when you increase the moisture content of the nail plate, it becomes highly flexible. Water can adversely affect the plate by increasing flexibility, altering shape, and lowering surface hardness.

When the nail plate absorbs water, it swells to accommodate the extra water molecules that have crowded between the layers of the nail plate. Soaking in water for more than sixty seconds allows water molecules to seep between the layers of nail cells and sheath them in this liquid lubricant. Now the layers can slide past each other with greater ease, making the nail plate easier to bend. A similar effect is seen when hair absorbs water, it becomes much easier to stretch without breaking. To see this effect in action, see the images shown in Volume 1, pg. 34.

Absorbed water causes the plate to swell, which may cause cracks to grow. Absorbed water will also make the nail plate's surface softer and much easier to damage. The softer the nail's surface, the more prone it will be to scratching, pitting, flaking, and peeling. Softened nail plates are easier to damage by physical actions such as prying, picking, scraping, filing, etc. When nail plates are softened by soaking in water, surface damage to the nail is more likely to occur. Water gets the blame, but heavy handed nail techs usually cause much of the surface damage. A good general rule to remember is, "when a nail plate is soaked in water or other solvents for more than sixty seconds, expect its surface to be more susceptible to damage for the next hour". ***Be Cautious!***

Hand washing for fifteen to twenty seconds is not expected to add excessive amounts of water to a nail plate. To help maintain appropriate levels of cleanliness in nail salons and services, clients should always wash their hands before receiving any type of nail service. Although healthy nails are generally resistant to the effects of water; when previously damaged nails are soaked in water for more than a few minutes they can more quickly absorb excessive amounts of water and can swell the nail plate. When the nail plate swells, this worsens existing cracks or splits, which can weaken the nail plate. Of course, this could also be what your teacher was referring to when she said water dried out the nail. Using proper terminology is important for any profession and the nail industry is no exception. Please help with this issue and always strive to use proper and professional nail terminology- this facilitates better understanding.

8: Special Topic Understand Seven Important Properties of Natural and Artificial Nails Part 1

There are seven important properties of natural and artificial nails that are often responsible for how your nails will behave in real-world situations. Interestingly, these same properties apply to both natural and artificial nail coatings. For instance, if a client snags their natural or artificial nail on something, how will that nail respond? Will it tear or crack or will it resist being damaged? This often depends on one or more of these important properties. Let's review them, so you can have a deeper understanding of how these properties can affect all types of nails. Nail techs and clients often use words such as strong, hard, tough, flexible, brittle or weak to describe their nails, but what do these terms really mean? Properly understanding these terms will help nail professionals make the right choices for client's nail care.

1. *Strength*- What is Strength? We use the word all the time in many ways; everything from the strength of a person's character to muscle strength training; but nails don't have muscles. Of course, they certainly can have lots of character as any fan of nail art knows and they can certainly be strong, in fact they can be too strong- even dangerously strong! Strength is defined as the ability of a material to "resist breaking under the stress of a heavy load or impact". Bridges are good examples. They must be strong enough to hold all the crossing cars. In this case, the cars are the heavy load. Drop a wine glass on a ceramic tile floor and it will not have the strength to resist the impact. For the same reason, a hard-ceramic tile will break if a heavy frying pan were dropped. The strength of a tree branch allows it to resist the extra load created during heavy wind. Our muscles must be strong enough to resist tearing apart when moving heavy loads. The strength of hair allows it to resist breakage while being brushed.

Why do nail plates need to be strong? That is because we use them like tools. All the bending, picking, prying, poking, scratching and clawing we do with our nails is proof of their strength. Strength isn't the only property that nail plates must possess. There are several other important properties to consider. Would you want nails like titanium alloy? It is very strong, but we don't want or need our nail plates to be that strong. Not so strong that the nail plate would rip away from the nail bed and matrix area if caught on something. It would be better if it broke instead, since the alternative would not be fun or pleasant and could cause serious, possibly irreversible damage to the nail bed and matrix. Also, if client's nails were that hard and inflexible, they could poke out someone's eye, maybe their own! Of course, we want strong nails, but not quite that strong. Right? It is important for the nail plate to break under certain conditions, so they must not be too strong. Nail plates are designed to break at some point before more serious, potentially permanent damage can occur.

This is one of the problems of the use of methyl methacrylate monomer (MMA), which is sometimes used as an ingredient in certain monomer liquid and polymer powder (L&P) formulations. MMA is too strong. Rather than break when impacted, the force will cause the natural nail to crack, rather than the artificial nail coating. In other words, an MMA nail coating is too strong to function properly as an artificial nail. There are other problems with the properties of MMA that make it an undesirable ingredient for artificial nails which are discuss in other questions, e.g. Volume 1, page 6.

2. *Hardness*- Many are confused about the unique property called hardness. A substance's hardness describes how resistant its surface is to scratching or denting. That's all, nothing else. Many incorrectly use the term hardness when they really mean strength. Hardness is not strength. Weak substances with low strength can be either very hard or very soft. Glass shatters easily, yet its surface is very hard. Diamond is the hardest known substance. Diamond can easily scratch glass, topaz or quartz. None of these materials can scratch the surface of a diamond because each is softer than diamond. That is an important concept to understand. By comparison to diamond, the nail plate is about five times softer; even so its surface hardness is very important. When nail plates become softer than normal, they are more easily scratched or stained or have a greater tendency to peel or become pitted. This is especially true when gouged or scraped to remove artificial nail coatings. Healthy nail plates need to be hard, but not too hard or they will be more susceptible to shattering and splitting. Overuse of certain nail hardening products may cause nail plates to become excessively or overly hardened and that can lead to brittleness, cracking, shatters, splitting, etc.

Clients may think they want nails that are as "hard as they can be", but they really don't. Which would you rather your nails resemble rubber or glass? Rubber is not nearly as hard as glass, but most would rather their nails were more flexible like rubber. Harder isn't always better! Nail hardeners offer a perfect example. Only use nail hardener/strengthener to reach the desired rigidity- then discontinue use until needed again. The same is true of artificial nail coatings of any type. If they are too brittle, service breakdown becomes more likely to occur. Too flexible and they can crack and peel. But adding a little "bend" to something "brittle" will almost always improve the situation. As the ancient philosopher, Confucius noted, *"The green reed which bends in the wind is stronger than the mighty oak which breaks in a storm."*

3. *Flexibility*- Confucius was no doubt speaking metaphorically about people, but none the less, "flexibility" is an extremely important property that allows a substance to bend. Flexible materials bend to absorb a strong force or impact and do this rather than to crack or break. As the quote above reminds us, anything that resists bending can be damaged when a sudden heavy load is applied. Normal healthy nail plates are highly flexible and will usually bend rather than break. Inflexible nails tend to break, rather than bend. Age, diet, health, exposure to water, cleaning agents and many other factors can influence nail plate flexibility. Repeated or long-term exposure to harsh cleaners and solvents can also make nail plates brittle and less flexible.

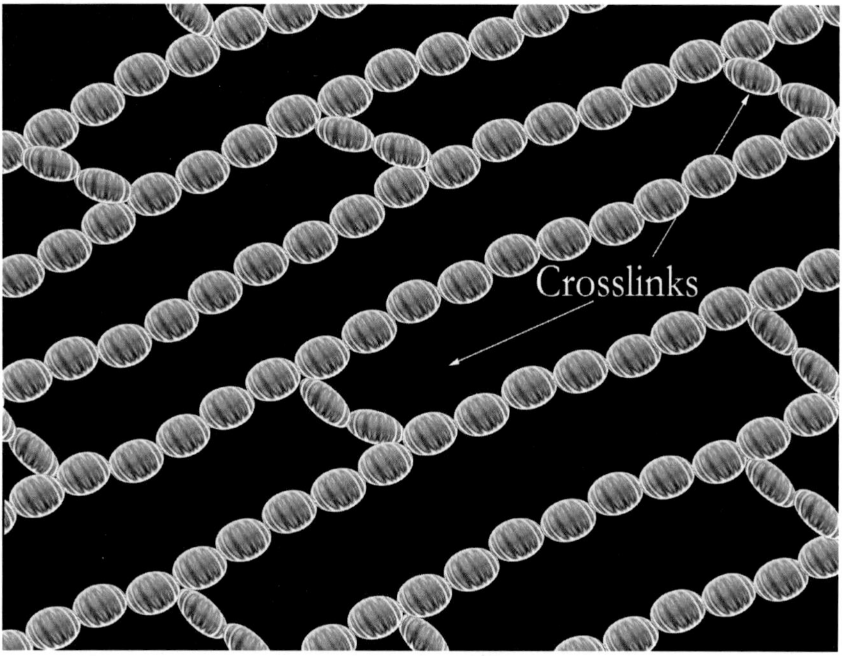

Image 5: This is an artistic representation of how many individual amino acids link together to create strands of the many types of proteins found inside the nail plate, e.g. keratin. These protein strands are the fundamental building blocks for both nails and hair. Some protein strands are "cross-linked" or joined together like rungs on a ladder which permanently holds them together. Cross-linking turns the many individual strands into a stronger, net-like structure that is much more resistant to bending, breaking or cracking.

Don't confuse flexibility with strength - they are quite different! Many things are very flexible, but have very little strength and the reverse is also true. Aluminum can pop-tops are an excellent example. They are very flexible, but bend them a few times and they will snap off. A sheet of paper is extremely flexible, yet a child can tear it easily. Systems that use cyanoacrylate, such as fiberglass wraps are extremely flexible. These can be more flexible than the natural nail, and therefore can't reinforce highly flexible nail plates. Natural or artificial nails that are too flexible can break and crack more easily. This helps explain why these types of nail systems are best used on nail plates that are not overly flexible. Unlike monomer liquid and polymer powder systems or UV gels, cyanoacrylate wraps do not offer much protection for weak, overly flexible nail plates. Nails certainly need some degree of flexibility, since we don't want the nail to be like the oak tree that breaks in a storm. That is another problem with using MMA monomer as an ingredient in nail coatings; this monomer liquid creates a coating that is not flexible and instead makes is highly rigid. These coatings don't bend with the natural nail, which is one of many reasons why nail coating products that contain MMA should be avoided. What we really want for both natural and artificial nails is for them to be both strong and flexible.

4. *Toughness-* We really want our nails to be tough! What is toughness and why do we want it for our nails? Toughness is the balanced combination of both strength and flexibility. When these two important properties are in balance, the result is a tough, durable material. Nylon fishing line is about the same thickness as ordinary cotton string, however is hundreds of times more resistant to breakage because it has a better balance of strength and flexibility. The plastic rings that hold together a six-pack of soda is another example of extremely tough material. Both healthy hair and nail plates are very tough materials- strength and flexibility in balance.

Toughness is one of the nail plates' most important properties! Nail plates must be able to protect the delicate tips of our fingers and toes. This helps explain why both natural nails and artificial nail coatings can become brittle or snap/split easily. When this occurs, it is an indication that strength and flexibility are out-of-balance. This occurs when there is too much strength and not enough flexibility, or the opposite, too much flexibility and not enough strength. Either way, the end result is that toughness is lost! Which means durability is lost and the nails become susceptible to damage. Nail plates that are too flexible can break more easily than normal nails, just as those that are too strong with little flexibility are more prone to breakage. You can see now how strength and flexibility are intertwined and directly linked. Natural and artificial nails must have both strength and flexibility.

5. *Brittleness-* This important property causes nails to break easily, even when very little stress or impact occurs. Our bones are a great example. Young children's bones are highly flexible. Bones lose flexibility as they age. Elderly people's bones are more brittle and more easily broken. When flexibility is lacking, nail plates can become brittle and break easily. When nail plates or coatings suddenly begin to crack, fracture or shatter- this can be a sign of brittleness. If a nail bends before then breaks, it is probably NOT brittle!

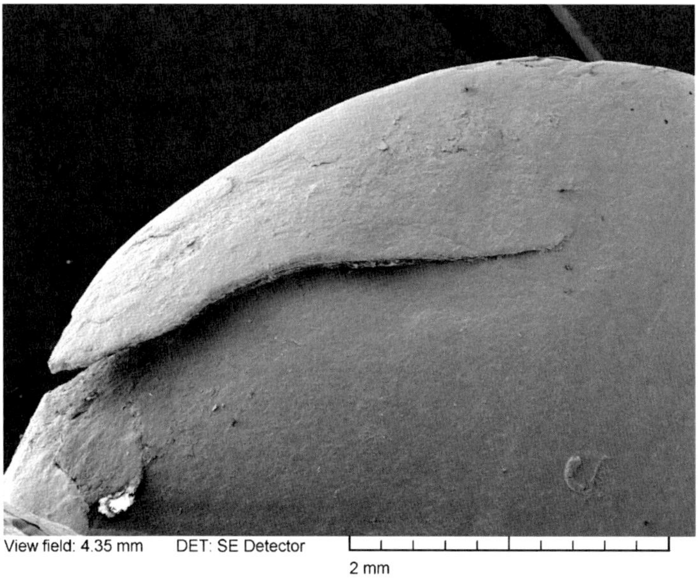

Image 6a: Brittle nails easily break, crack or shatter without much bending

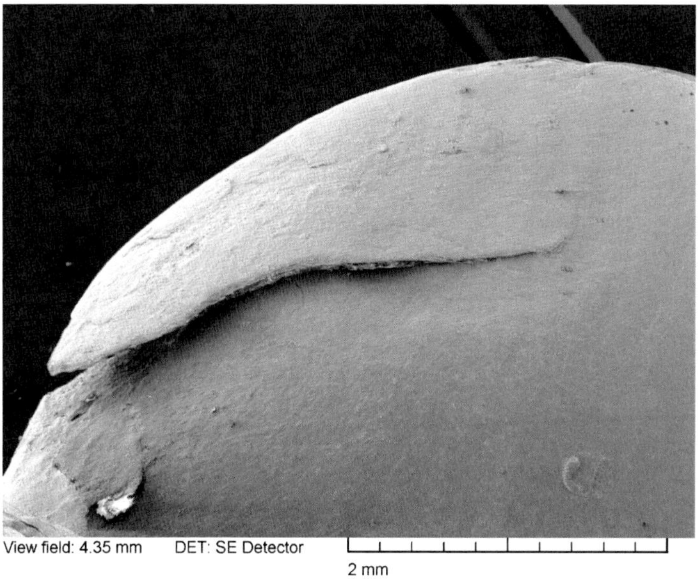

Image 6b: 3D image of nail plate crack.
***Red/Cyan** 3D glasses required.*

In other words, when brittle nails are impacted, snagged or otherwise damaged, they tend to break easily, without a lot of force. If the clients claim they were doing nothing and the nail "just broke", they could be exaggerating or their nails may have become brittle over time. Artificial nails aren't made brittle, the brittleness develops over time, it is usually a few weeks to a month before some become noticeably brittle. This could be just the way that particular product is formulated or brittleness can also be a sign of improper curing. When brittle natural or artificial nails break, this can be accompanied by a snapping sound. Glass is an example of a naturally brittle material. Like nails, glass can be made tougher to reduce brittleness and lower the tendency for it to shatter. Age, diet, health, cleaning agents, solvents and many other factors can influence nail plate brittleness.

What reverses brittleness? Once nails become brittle, what can be done? Toughness is a balance of strength and flexibility. When this balance is lost, strength can overpower flexibility to result in brittleness. In other words, brittleness occurs when flexibility is lost. The best way to address this issue is the use of a high-quality nail oil. These are designed to absorb into the nail plate and by doing so, they increase the flexibility of the nail plate and artificial nail coating. Just like leather conditioners reduce brittleness in leather, so will nail oils do for natural and artificial nails. They do so by restoring flexibility and bringing it back into balance with strength. Nail oils can penetrate the natural nail and all nail coatings, except for some UV cured nail coatings with surfaces that resist penetration by nail oils. This is also true of solvents such as acetone. For instance, it is very difficult for acetone to penetrate the so-called "hard UV gel" nail coatings, making them more difficult to remove.

6. *Solvent Resistance*- Solvents are liquids that dissolve solids or other liquids. Water is a great example of a solvent. Water dissolves sugar, salt and many, many other substances. In fact, water can dissolve more substances than any other liquid, which is why it is called the "Universal Solvent". Without the solvent properties of water, life could not exist as we know it. Water doesn't dissolve either the natural or artificial nails, because both surfaces are solvent-resistant, at least to water. Solvent-resistance is an important property for natural and artificial nails. Nail plates can absorb small amounts of solvents, but not be dissolved by them, as water demonstrates.

The water content of a natural nail is typically about 15%, but when exposed to water, then nail plate water content can double to 30%. This helps explain why water soluble substances can absorb more quickly into the nail plate than substances that are not water soluble. Artificial nails are much more resistant to water than the natural nail and will not absorb significant amounts. However, these do absorb other solvents such as acetone. Even so, you don't want your artificial nail coatings being destroyed when nail polish is removed by solvent, so some degree of solvent resistance is needed. Acetone can penetrate most artificial nails and begin to break them down, usually within ten to twenty minutes. Nail coating resistance to solvents like acetone can vary widely. This largely depends on the nail coating formulation. Some are designed to be easily attacked by acetone or other solvents and therefore remove easily.

MMA is notoriously resistant to both water and acetone, as are some types of UV curing nail gels. MMA and some UV gels can take an hour or more to be affected by acetone, making them more difficult to properly and carefully remove. If fast acting solvents like acetone have a difficult time penetrating an artificial nail coating, then expect that nail coating will have a difficult time absorbing nail oils, as well. This is a great way to determine if a nail oil can penetrate, by examining the acetone resistance of the artificial nail coating. The faster and easier the coating is attacked by acetone, the easier it will be for nail oils to penetrate the surface to increase flexibility. A nail coating that takes more than forty-five minutes to remove in acetone is much less likely to absorb nail oil, while a nail coating that removes in thirty minutes will more quickly absorb these oils. This test doesn't hold true for nail plates, since they don't dissolve in solvents. Natural nails have built-in channels that transmit naturally occurring oils from the nail bed to the nail plate and nail plates typically contain about 2-5% oily compounds that help keep the nail plate flexible.

There is a myth that says since the nail plate has no sebaceous oil glands like skin and the scalp, that nail plate can't contain oils. Not true, this myth assumes that all natural oils in the body come from sebaceous oil glands in the skin, but that's not correct. The nail bed and underlying tissues also produce natural oils, such as squalene, which is found in raw olive oils. There is very little squalene in highly refined olive oils, since the squalene is removed to help improve the clarity of the oil. Here's a hint, warming a nail oil to slightly above body temperature, e.g. 100°F or 38°C, will significantly increase the rate of penetration into the plate. This is especially true for brittle nails.

7. *Wear-* Resistance to wear (aka "wearing out") is the ability to resist abrasion or rubbing. Wear is an important property for the nail plate and artificial nail coatings to have. Tough, hard surfaces can be quickly worn away by using an abrasive with an even harder surface. Here's what I mean: on a 1-10 scale, diamonds have a hardness of 10 and fingernails hardness is 2. Nail plates are that low in hardness largely because they contain a lot of water. Artificial nail coatings vary widely in hardness, but most are between 2-3 hardness. Therefore, it is indeed true that artificial nail coatings often provide a tougher and harder protective coating with improved wear resistance. Many nail files are coated with a hard, crystalline mineral called "silicon carbide". Silicon carbide is inexpensive and has a hardness of 9, that's nearly as hard as diamonds- no wonder these files are so highly effective.

Diamond grit nail files are the most effective and like all abrasives, need to be used properly and carefully to avoid over filing the nail plate or removing too much of the nail coating. The white colored nail files are usually coated with aluminum oxide, a white, softer abrasive material with a 7.5 hardness. It about 25% softer than diamond and 15% softer than black silicon carbide, but still about 60% harder than natural nails and about 50% harder than artificial nail coatings. Files made with diamond or silicon carbide are more aggressive and have a greater potential to damage the nail plate than aluminum oxide. But any nail file can damage the nail plate if used in an overly aggressive manner... even natural nail buffers! It is important to note that when comparing the exact same grit size and the same downward pressure: Diamond is noticeably more aggressive than silicon carbide which is noticeably more aggressive than aluminum oxide- all due to the property called "hardness". The nail plate may be tough and durable, but it has very low surface hardness and can wear away quickly when abraded.

Image 7a: Nail plate filed with a 120 grit abrasive.

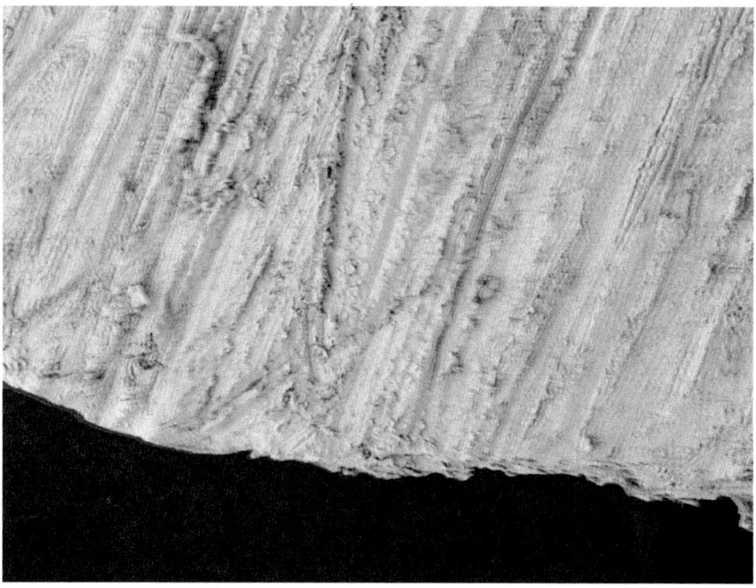

Image 7b: 3D image of nail plate filed with a 120 grit abrasive.
***Red/Cyan** 3D glasses required.*

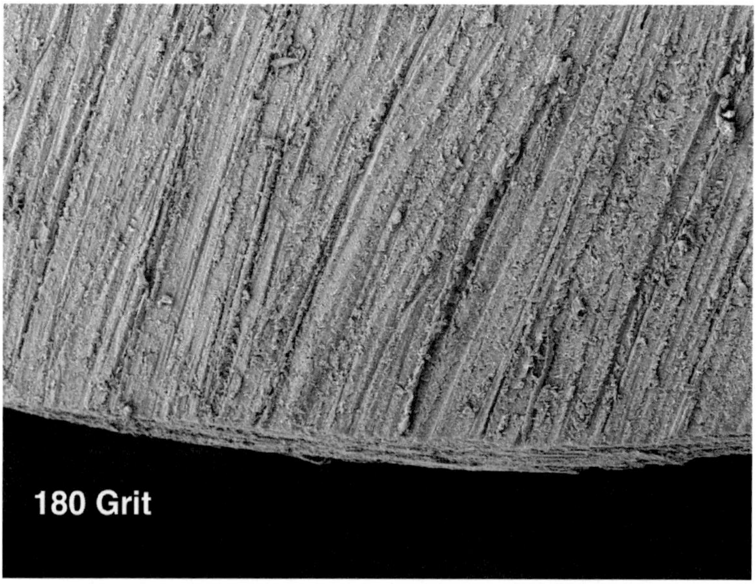

Image 8a: Nail plate filed with a 180 grit abrasive.

*Image 8b: 3D image of nail plate filed with a 180 grit abrasive. **Red**/Cyan 3D glasses required.*

Image 9a: Nail plate filed with a 240 grit abrasive.

Image 9b: 3D image of nail plate filed with a 240 grit abrasive. ***Red****/Cyan 3D glasses required.*

Abrasive particles scratch away masses of surface nail cells- that is how they work as you can see in the photos. Large particles of the lower grit files create wider and deeper scratches, while smaller particles on higher grit files will create tinier scratches. This explains why heavy grit abrasives can cause excessive thinning and damage to the nail plate. Heavy pressure can drive the scratches deeper and increase nail plate thinning. The free edge can also be worn down, but not very easily. Not surprisingly, nail plates and artificial nails having greater toughness- will also be more resistant to wear. One way to make something wear-resistant is to make it tougher. For brittle natural nails, the solution is to increase flexibility, e.g. hot oil treatments.

So, to recap, our seven properties are: Strength, Flexibility, Hardness, Toughness, Brittleness, Solvent Resistance and Wear. If you take the time to understand these properties and use that understanding to troubleshoot client's nail issues, you'll be way ahead of the game. Understanding these properties provides a deeper understanding about how and why natural and artificial nails behave the way they do. With this deeper understanding, you can use your knowledge to keep both natural and artificial nails in top shape!

16:5 I have noticed that older ladies, say 60 + have a lot thicker nails that are sometimes challenging to cut even with professional equipment! Also, sometimes this is accompanied by a thickening of the nail bed underneath which attaches itself to the nail plate as it grows. I never cut the nail bed as this can cause all manner of problems, least of which is bleeding. What causes thickening of the nail plate and bed in this age group?

For both healthy toes and fingers, the thickness of the nail plate is determined solely by the length of the nail matrix where the nail plate cells are created. The matrix does not suddenly grow longer, so the nail plate under most circumstances won't suddenly begin to grow thicker. Several things can cause the plate to appear thickened. For example, if the layers of the nail plate begin to separate; the plate will appear to thicken. An example is a roll of toilet paper. The roll will appear to thicken when it becomes wet, not because there is more paper on the roll, but because the layers are slightly farther apart.

Thickening can happen when the nail plate is infected by fungal organisms. Fungi eat keratin, which causes the plate to loosen and come apart. Minor damage or constant irritation to the nail bed itself can cause it to produce some nail cells. Under normal circumstances, all nail cells in the plate come from the matrix area at the base of the nail plate. However, this can change if the nail is injured. Under some circumstances the nail bed can contribute additional nail cells to the bottom of the nail plate, likely as a protective measure.

One more thing that should be understood. It is unlikely that the nail bed would remain attached to the plate, but the hyponychium can be firmly attached and be dragged outward with the nail plate as it grows. This can happen on both toes and fingers. The hyponychium is a seal that protects the nail bed from infection. When the nail is injured, sometimes this tissue remains attached to the bottom of the nail plate, it stretches as it grows, which can become painful. You are correct, this would bleed if cut.

In medical terms, when living skin is abnormally stretched like this, it is called “pterygium”. This word is sometimes misused by nail professionals when applied to normal tissue. Pterygium is an abnormal growth of living skin and can occur on several parts of the body, including the nails. What causes this abnormal growth? When it occurs under the free edge, it is often caused by injury which is another reason why it is unwise to cut this tissue. Doing so will only worsen the condition and can lead to infections. Even though the plate can appear to thicken due to fungal infections, infected nail plates are being broken down and are coming apart to create an illusion that the nail plate has grown thicker. These infections often cause the plate to crumble or come apart more easily.

Infection, disease, injury, irritation or allergic reactions can cause the fingernails to form pterygium. On the toes, growth of pterygium is often a result of injury or diseases. The injury doesn’t have to be severe; but it won’t be caused by minor injury. Some believe injury can also contribute to nail plate thickening, e.g. constant or repeated injury or irritation to the toes, but that is questionable based on how the nail plate grows. It would be best to refer them to a podiatrist or their own medical doctor, even so I’d also recommend talking to these clients about their foot wear so they can identify any irritation or injury to that area since this can also lead to onycholysis. If the condition becomes painful or infected, they should be referred to a medical professional.

21:1 I’ve heard that the nail won’t absorb anything and I hear it absorbs just about everything. What are the facts?

The nail plate’s upper layer and nail surface are very resistant and prevent most substances from absorbing at all. This is one reason why a healthy natural nail plate is a good barrier. Only water and certain naturally occurring oil soluble substances such as squalene can penetrate easily through the nail plate.

An oil soluble substance is exactly what it sounds like, substances that will dissolve in certain oils, but mostly likely will not dissolve in water. Sugar and salt are good examples of water soluble substances that don't dissolve in oil. Substances that dissolve in water are called hydrophilic (hy-dro-phil-ic), which means water loving.

"Hydro" means water in ancient Greek and "philic" means loving. Substances that dissolve in oil are called "lipophilic" (ly-po-phil-ic) which means oil loving. Lipos is from the ancient Greek word for fat. Lipophilic means fat or oil loving. So, a lipophilic substance is soluble in oil. Some substances are soluble in both water and oil, but not many fall into that category. Rubbing alcohol is an example of a substance that dissolves in both water and oil.

Not many substances are soluble in both, in fact it is considered an unusual property. Squalene is an oil soluble component of natural nail, hair, and skin oils. It is also found in raw olives, but is found in lessor amounts in highly refined olive oils. The refining process makes the olive oil look clear and taste better, but this removes much of the squalene from the olive oil. The squalene is then purified and sold as a cosmetic ingredient mainly for hair and skin care applications.

Water is the only substance that moves quickly though the nail plate and it moves much faster through the nail plate than it does through skin. Oily substances move more slowly through the nail plate than water. Migration of substance through the nail plate occurs only for substances with a chemical structure that mimics the natural oils in the nail plate. Oil concentrations in the plate can increase with each additional topical application. The oil concentration in the nail plate can more than double from a low 3% to 6% or maybe even 7%, with repeated applications. Repeated applications will allow the nail plate to maintain higher levels of oil in the nail plate. One reason is, there are pathways between the nail cells that allow for the passage of oil or water, see Image 4.

Since oil and water don't mix, there are passages that channel water through the plate and other passages dedicated to channeling oily substances through the nail plate. There are probably many more channels for water than oil, but the smaller size of water molecules also help water to move quicker through the nail plate.

Application of heat can also speed penetration of oil soluble substances into the nail plate, which is why hot oil manicures are more effective. Some oily substances have chemical structures that are very different from the natural nail. These types of substances are not compatible with the nail plate's chemical structure and therefore cannot penetrate at all. Mineral oil and many massage oils cannot penetrate, which is why they are used to provide long lasting lubrication and slip when applied to the skin. Mineral oil remains on the surface of the nail plate and skin and doesn't absorb. Any oil or oily substance that won't penetrate the skin is also unlikely to penetrate nails.

Some other well-known examples of oils known for their ability to penetrate the natural nail are jojoba, coconut and avocado oil. There are some substances which can penetrate the top surface of the nail plate, but can't move beyond the upper layers of the nail plate and therefore they become trapped inside the plate. Nicotine stains are a good example.

Nicotine molecules are shaped like two interconnected rings. Nicotine penetrates the surface of the nail plate, but its bulky shape prevents it from going any deeper. That's because the plate is such a good barrier and it is highly selective about what substances it allows to absorb. As more and more nicotine builds up near the surface, the stain becomes darker and darker, eventually turning so dark brown, it can appear to be almost as black. If the surface of the nail plate is damaged, some substances will penetrate more easily. But even these will be trapped in the upper layers of the nail plate and not able to penetrate beyond into the middle layers. Of course, if the nail plate is cracked completely through to the nail bed, then great care should be taken.

Substances applied over these types of breaks or cracks can completely penetrate and gain easier access to the nail bed below. The nail plate is a good barrier to absorption, which also explains why topical anti-fungal medical treatments don't work very well. It is very difficult to get enough of the anti-fungal ingredient into the nail plate, even when special penetration enhancers are used. The nail is a powerful barrier. Only water has the ability to easily penetrate the nail. That's not too surprising. Water is a powerful chemical solvent.

Most don't think of water in those terms, but that's exactly what it is. Normally, it is difficult to completely penetrate through the plate. Complete penetration is pretty unlikely to occur with any cosmetic products, since most ingredients have no ability to penetrate completely through the nail plate. Even high quality, penetrating nail oils don't completely penetrate. These oils build up inside the nail plate and become trapped, which makes them very difficult to remove again, even when hands are washed excessively.

In short, when asked, if substances penetrate the nail plate, a "yes or no" answer just doesn't apply. It's more correct to say, that in general, most substances cannot get past the outer surface of the nail plate, while some substances can penetrate into the upper layers and become trapped and remain there. Only a very few select substances can penetrate through the nail plate. All in all, the natural nail is a powerful barrier that's not easy to overcome!

27:1 Why do my clients cuticles grow thicker during the winter. Are they doing that because of the cold weather?

The most misunderstood part of the fingernail is the cuticle. Some complain their cuticles are growing extra thick, but that doesn't really happen. They are confusing the cuticle with the proximal nail fold. It's easy to do, even doctors and scientists are confused about this issue. Here's what's known and presently understood. This answer contains recently updated information about nail anatomy that I've obtained from leading dermatologists and pathologists.

1. The cuticle is attached directly to the nail plate. If what you are looking at is a thin layer of tissue directly attached to nail plate only; it ***is*** the cuticle. The cuticle rides the nail plate and comes from the underside of the living skin and is created by very thin layer of specialized tissue called "eponychium".

2. The proximal nail fold is the living skin at the base fingernail. Any visible skin permanently attached to the proximal nail fold is **not** cuticle.

3. If the skin is attached to both the nail plate and the proximal nail fold, it is really just part of the proximal nail fold, and *is* ***not*** the cuticle.

4. When the proximal nail fold is cut or damaged, it will grow thicker to protect itself. This isn't an overgrowth of the cuticle; it's a hardening and thickening of the proximal nail fold. This happens for the same reason that the foot develops a thicker callus when the skin is subjected to increased pressure or rubbing.

5. The cuticle will not grow back thicker when removed from the nail plate; nor will it grow thicker during the cold season. The cuticle can't grow, because it is dead tissue. It is shed from the eponychium and rides the nail plate as it moves toward the free edge. Why? To serve as a seal to prevent infectious organisms from getting under the skin or into the nail matrix area.

6. The cuticle will not bleed when cut, it is dead and has no blood supply, since it is detached from the living skin and attached to the nail plate instead.

7. If the tissue bleeds when cut back too much, this is part of the proximal nail fold and ***is not*** the cuticle.

8. If the cuticle and proximal nail fold seem to merge together and become "overgrown", this is usually caused by damage or injury to the living eponychium, often as a disease

condition or some other unknown issue. This type of tissue is pterygium, which is an abnormal growth of skin.

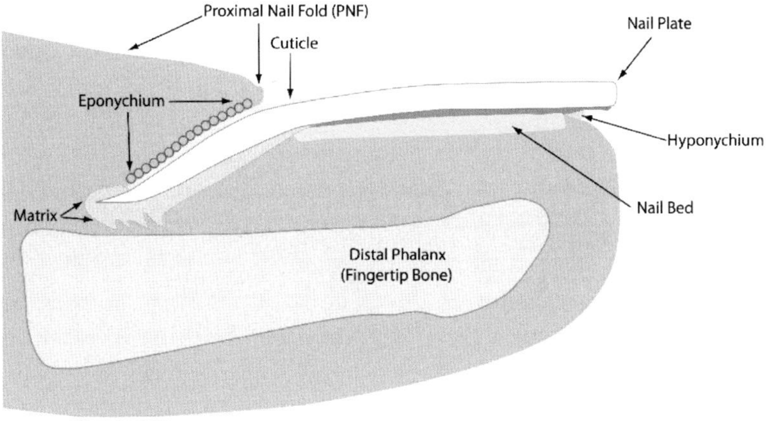

Image 10: Cross-section of a human fingertip.

In these cases, when the nail professional trims off this dry, crusty skin this can cause the proximal nail fold to grow back faster to protect itself from this injury. That's why the best solution is to avoid cutting the skin. Instead, treat hardened tissue with high quality nail oil and repeat this daily. Also, performing weekly hot oil treatments will help a lot. After thirty to forty days, this dry crusty-looking skin will begin to flake off and eventually will disappear to reveal the healthy tissue underneath. Do not cut or remove the hardened layer on the proximal nail fold, it will just make matters worse- just like a dog chasing its own tail!

I'd also like to add this about the term pterygium. Contrary to what some teach, this is not another name for the dead tissue on the nail plate. Pterygium is a medical condition that occurs on different parts of the body, including eyes and fingernails. In general, the term is used to describe any wing-like and triangular-shaped tissue on the neck, eyes, elbow, knees, ankles or fingers. The word comes from the Greek word for wing and refers only to abnormal growths of skin that are stretched into a wing-like shape.

Pterygium commonly occurs on the eyeballs of people exposed to lots of sunlight or wind. This explains why those who surf or fish on the ocean are sometimes affected. It can occur on the nail plate, but is considered an abnormal medical condition often caused by burns, serious injury, damage, disease and possibly allergic reactions. Cuticle tissue is normal and is not an abnormal growth, so it can't be pterygium.

This term and others are creating confusion in the industry. I know, everyone is confused. But as research continues and new information is learned, slowly the facts are emerging. For clarity's sake, my recommendation is that all educators and manufacturers only use the word "pterygium" to describe abnormal stretching of the proximal nail fold or the hyponychium. I don't fault any company that's confused about this issue, but I would encourage them to research and teach the facts. It's time to move past the use of incorrect terminology. It's time for change and all responsible companies should help to lead the way. It's a new day and we should all be doing our best to always use the correct terminology when describing the natural nail. You have my commitment to continue researching new discoveries and passing that information on to nail professionals.

28:2 Can some nail oils make my nails grow faster? If so, which ones and how do they work?

This question is an example of how important it is to use the correct words when speaking about nails and nail products or you may fool yourself into thinking things that are not true! No cosmetic, including nail oils can make the nail grow any "faster". Anything that can make the nail grow faster or speed up growth is considered a medical drug, not a cosmetic. Such a claim is not allowed for cosmetic products and currently there are no known medical drugs that can speed up nail growth. Nor are there any vitamins which can make the nails grow faster. Some improperly claim that biotin makes the nail grow faster, but there is very little evidence of this.

There is a very limited amount of evidence that biotin can reduce nail plate brittleness, but these have only been a few small studies and a few dermatologist claims it helped a few patents, but not most. High quality nail oil can help the nail to grow longer. How is that? Isn't this also a medical drug or medicine claim? No, it is not the same as speeding up nail growth. To make the nail grow "faster" requires making the nail matrix work faster to produce nail cells more quickly. No cosmetic can do this and it is not an allowed cosmetic claim. Nail oils reduce brittleness in the nail plate by increasing flexibility.

How? When certain nail oils absorb into the nail plate, they concentrate between the layers in the upper part of the nail plate where most of the plate's brittleness occurs. The oils add lubrication between these layers, allowing them to slide more easily and therefore bend more easily without breaking. Unlike biotin, there is plenty of evidence that penetrating nail oils do indeed reduce brittleness of the nail plate and that they work fairly quickly! Penetrating nail oils contain "lipids", naturally occurring fatty acids and their derivatives, which absorb to add flexibility and reduce brittleness making the nail plate tougher and less likely to break. They can allow the nail plate to grow longer than it normally would, rather than to break off just past the free edge. It is perfectly reasonable to expect a good quality nail oil to "help" the nail plate grow longer; while it is unreasonable to expect any cosmetic product or supplement to make the nails grow faster.

My advice is to skip the nutritional nail growth supplements and use a high quality, absorbing nail oil regularly to improve the condition of the nail plate. These are far more likely to help the nail growth than biotin or any other nail supplement. I recommend using professional quality nail oils, especially those which contain low viscosity, light weight oils such as avocado oil. Heavy oils and waxes are less likely to penetrate in significant amounts. Keratin doesn't penetrate the nail plate either, and will remain on the surface. A good rule of thumb to remember is, any oil that won't quickly penetrate the skin is very unlikely to penetrate the nail plate.

30:4 I was told that the bonds holding together the nail plate run longitudinally to help stop lengthwise splits and this meant that it was better to "remove shine" in direction of nail growth or these bonds could be broken. But you said before that the direction of nail filing doesn't matter. Can you explain?

The image below shows how keratin fibrils inside the nail cells all lay in one direction across the width of the nail plate. I explain how this prevents cracking down the length of the nail plate. This arrangement of keratin fibrils causes the nail plate to crack across its width. How? These fibrils act like speed bumps to slow down the spread of cracks that would split the plate. Instead they cause these cracks to change directions and to run between the keratin fibrils, not across them. This arrangement does influence how cracks spread, but this has little to do with filing the surface of the nail plate. Filing doesn't cause cracks in the nail plate, it just abrades away the surface of the nail plate. Each nail cell is connected to other nail cells from many different directions, including from above and below. I have personally conducted studies on various directions of filing did not show that in a specific direction caused additional nail damage. In short, I know of no reason why the nail plate should only be filed in the direction of growth. It is far more important to use a light touch and avoid abrasives lower than 180 grit on the natural nail, 240 grit is best for natural nails, in my own opinion.

Image 11a: Keratin fibrils inside a nail plate cell at high magnifications.

Image 11b: Keratin fibrils inside a nail plate cell at high magnifications. ***Red/Cyan*** *3D glasses required.*

35:1 Why do nail plates snap off at the free edge rather than split?

There are many reinforcing bonds holding nails cells together. These form randomly in all directions, so it would be expected that the plate would be equally resistant to cracking in all directions. Clearly, that is not the case. The nail plate is highly prone to breaking in one direction, across the width of the plate as shown in Image 6 (above). Only in an unusual circumstance does a break or split occur down the length of the plate. The reason for this is the internal structure of each nail cell.

Each nail cell is filled with many short strands of keratin called "fibrils" and they have the appearance of tiny fibers. These fibers aren't randomly distributed, but instead are uniformly stacked into neat piles, much like logs of wood are stacked. These stacks of fibrils lay across the width of the nail plate with their ends pointing toward the sidewalls, see Image 11. This arrangement makes it much easier for a crack to travel between the fibrils, rather than across or through them. This keratin fiber arrangement leads the cracks to turn toward the sidewalls and prevents cracks from spreading down the length of the plate.

Cracks move like water flowing downhill; they take the path of least resistance. This helps to prevent the nail plate from splitting open to expose the underlying nail bed. In this way, the nail plate protects itself from catastrophic injuries that can lead to serious infections. The plate can split down its length, but when it does, often the crack follows a deep groove that formed in the nail plate.

39:4 Does soaking in acetone changed the structure of the nail plate? Will it make the nails curl more?

Typically, the nail plate is soaked in acetone for ten minutes or more which can temporarily remove approximately 2 or 3% (possibly more) of the water content of the nail plate. That's enough to temporarily alter the shape of the nail plate, but this will not affect the nail plate's actual structure. I define "structure" as the way in which the nail cells join and make the nail plate. Acetone can't change the structure at all.

The same thing occurs when a sponge changes shape as it dries out, but the sponge's structure hasn't changed at all. When water is put back into the sponge, it would revert to its wet shape. If the structure changed, then it would not do so and would instead become permanently deformed.

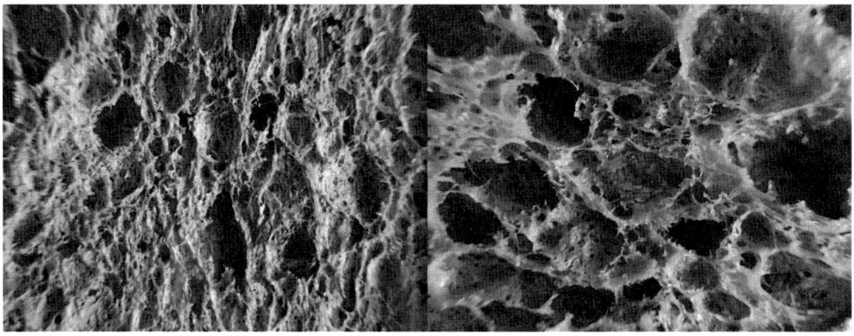

Image 12: Dry sponge Wet sponge

Even though acetone can NOT deform the structure of the nail plate, it will temporarily remove some of the moisture, especially near the surface of the nail plate. After removing the nail plate from the acetone, the nail plate's lost moisture will be automatically replaced by moisture from the underlying nail bed and surrounding tissues, as shown in Image 2. If the shape changes, this will be much more noticeable on thin or highly flexible nail plates and probably not as noticeable on thicker nail plates with less flexibility. Acetone could never completely remove all oil or water, just a small amount. For example, a nail plate that contained 15% water and 4% oil, after soaking in acetone for 30 minutes might now contain 12% water and 3% oil. All the lost water and oil is mostly removed from the surface and this should certainly be replaced within approximately eight to twelve hours, maybe faster for some nails. Likely any changes in the shape of the nail plate should be reversed in hours, not days.

Acetone can do the same to the skin; remove some water and oil, mostly from just the surface of the skin. It's not likely to penetrate deeper in significant quantities, it escapes too quickly by evaporation. This is one of the reasons acetone is the preferred solvent for nail coating removal. It is safe to use for this application and doesn't harm the nail plate. The main concern with acetone is that it is highly flammable, so use cautiously to avoid fires. Use this solvent wisely and responsibly!

Natural Nail Service/Treatment

6:2 Is calcium good for the natural nail?

I don't know of any evidence that demonstrates that oral ingestion of calcium does anything positive for nails, at all! Nail plates do contain a very small amount of calcium, but that's likely deposited there by the water we wash our hands with. Calcium is found only on the surface of the nail plate, not in deeper layers, which further supports that the calcium comes from hand washing. To my knowledge, the nail plate doesn't need calcium and doesn't benefit from it at all. Of course, should any convincing evidence become available to support this myth, I'm happy to review and reconsider. However, until then I would not recommend calcium supplements since they don't appear to benefit the nail. The same is true for topical application of calcium; this can't help the nail plate either.

10:2 Does the nail plate absorb any chemicals found in the products we use? I want to be able to provide my clients with the most accurate information possible. I know our nail plates can absorb moisture via water and oil but do they absorb acetone and other chemicals through gel polish, acrylics or regular nail lacquers?

An unbroken nail plate is very difficult to penetrate, and that's what I believe you are asking. Our skin and nails are a barrier between us and the outside word. Our nail beds are covered with this tough, highly impenetrable nail plate barrier that prevents penetration. Other than nail oils and water, not much else will penetrate very far past the upper layers of the nail plate. A good example would be a smoker's stain on the nail plate. The tars and nicotine absorb into the nail plate, these can't absorb very deeply, so instead they pool just under the upper surface of the nail plate to form a stain that becomes increasingly darker with additional exposure. The reason the stain becomes darker is because the nicotine (and tars) can't penetrate any deeper, so they collect in one area. Acetone is also very volatile and evaporates too quickly from the nail plate to penetrate very far.

Other ingredients don't penetrate either. Besides water and nail oils, any ingredient in nail products that does penetrate the surface will be restricted to the upper layers of the nail plate. So, in short, it is unlikely that any significant amounts of the nail products you mentioned can absorb beyond the surface or upper layers of the nail plate.

11:7 We have a difficult salon client that has ridges in her nail plates. She doesn't allow me or any of the other nail techs to buff them because she says that the buffing will cause them to crack and bleed. I explained to her that light buffing will not make them bleed. What is a good way to explain to her that buffing is ok?

I agree with your client. It is common for nail technicians to buff the nail plate smooth to remove so-called "ridges", but surprisingly, there are no ridges on the nail plate to be removed, see Image 24. The nail plate can't suddenly start growing ridges. That's not possible due to the way the nail matrix produces nail cells. Instead, the nail plate develops shallow grooves where the aging or damaged nail matrix isn't working as efficiently and is now making fewer new nail cells in certain areas.

It is normal to see shallow grooves on nail plates of people older than thirty and is considered a normal sign of healthy aging. I don't recommend filing to remove these high points. Why? That just reduces the thickness of the entire nail plate and the nail plate can be sustainably weakened. Buffing away these so-called "ridges" will just thin the nail plate down to be as thick as the bottom of the deepest groove on the plate. The file just strips away the top layer. Yikes! That's a lot of nail plate being removed. It is far better to keep the client's nail plates thick! Nail coatings, including nail polish, don't adhere well to overly thin nail plates.

The reduction in plate thickness often leads to poor adhesion of any applied nail coating. Excessive plate thinning can also cause the nail's surface to peel excessively and/or crack at the free edge. When the nail plate develops these grooves, rather than filing the surface smooth, it is far better to use an opaque base coat to fill and cover the grooves. This will maintain the thickness and integrity of the nail plate. Overlaying the nail plate with a thin layer of any type of artificial nail coating can also camouflage the groove and reinforce/strengthen the nail plate, while improving its appearance without over thinning. In the long run, this is a far superior method for improving the appearance of the client's nail plates. There is no need to make the nail plate thinner, when it's relatively easy and better to cover and hide normal grooves that run the length of the plate.

11:9 I use a few brands of decorated adhesive nail strips. When I remove them, some clients develop large whitish patches on the nail plate. Why does this happen and how can I stop it. My clients are blaming me.

I understand your concern and if I understand your question, my advice in this case is to warn your clients not to remove these types of products by themselves. They are likely to cause this type of problem if they improperly remove these types of nail coatings. It is the upward force on the nail plate surface that causes chunks of nail to be pulled up, which leads to surface damage. On a large scale, this creates surface white spots when any type of nail coating is too forcefully removed. Proper removal is important for all types of applied nail coatings, including adhesive nail strips of any type. Many retail users end up damaging their own nails because they improperly remove these decorative nail strips. Most often, they don't allow sufficient time for the remover solvents to do their job and attempt to speed up the process by peeling them off with too much force.

If you take short cuts, or don't use the proper equipment or lamps and don't follow the manufacturer's directions, the potential for problems such as nail damage increases. I recommend reaching out to the manufacturer and/or distributors to get more information or recommendations related to proper and safe use then pay attention to those recommendations. They should know best when it comes to their own products! Don't you think?

13:1 Does it make sense to file the natural nail before applying a nail coating that's designed to be removed every two weeks?

Overfilling of the nail plate is a significant problem in many nail salons. Assuming the nail grew at normal rates, the nail plate would be filed eight times while on its journey toward reach the free edge. That's a lot of potential damage waiting to happen, so I would not recommend this practice. I can't imagine why anyone would do this to their client's nails. Additional nail damage can occur when these types of coatings are improperly removed. I recommend that nail technicians file the surface of the nail plate as little possible using only a fine abrasive and avoiding a heavy hand. The greater the downward pressure, the greater the potential for damage. Many advanced nail coating systems require minimal or no filing to achieve the necessary levels of adhesion, there are also other options you can explore. My recommendation is to find a system that doesn't require excessive filing, if that's needed to get good adhesion, something else is not right and is likely why there is adhesion loss. Don't be willing to over-thin the nail plate, instead find a solution that keeps the nail plate thick and heathy. Nail coatings of all types have trouble adhering to overly thin and overly flexible nail plates.

28:4 A nail professional in Ukraine asks, what oils are best for adding moisture to nails and are different oils better for hair or skin?

Moisturizers are misunderstood. Contrary to what some may believe, oils can't add any moisture to nails, skin or hair, but they can prevent "dryness", so this causes some confusion. When moisturizing is added, that increases “water” concentration inside nails, skin or hair. As you probably already know, water and oil don’t mix. The water content of any cosmetic oil is nearly zero. They are considered “anhydrous” or “without water”. Oils and water can exist together in a cosmetic lotion or cream, but only if they are mixed with a special type of ingredient called an “emulsifier”. Emulsifiers are used to create many types of oil and water blends. Many foods, such as salad dressings, mayonnaise and ice cream are all made possible by emulsifiers and without them these ingredients would quickly separate.

Creams and lotions can increase the moisture content of nails, skin or hair because they contain significant amounts of water as an ingredient. Oils by themselves can also increase the moisture content of nails and skin, but they do this in a different way than many understand. Oils coat the nails and skin with thin film that forms a moisture resistant barrier. Some oils can penetrate and will create a barrier in the upper layers of the skin. Underneath this barrier, moisture can build up, thus raising the water content of nails or skin, but not for hair. Why? A steady supply of water travels from nail bed to the nail plate surface, just as it does from the dermis to the skin’s outer surface as shown in Image 2. This water migration is slowed down by oils. Water migration through the epidermis is called “trans-epidermal water loss” or TEWL. Cosmetic scientists use special instruments to measure the TEWL to determine the effectiveness of skin lotions, creams and oils. Lower water loss (less water escaping from skin) means a product is a more effective moisturizer. This type of water migration doesn’t occur in a shaft of hair, so oils can’t moisturize the hair. Some oils provide additional benefits by increasing the flexibility in nails, skin or hair. As I explained in a previous question, nail oils add lubrication which allows the various layers to slide across each other, increasing flexibility. Oils also soften each of these to make their surfaces less hard. Some don’t penetrate at all, and remain on top of the skin. Those that sit on top of the skin are called “occlusive agents”.

That term may sound like something out of a spy thriller, but the word "occlude" simply means "to block" or "obstruct". Mineral oil is an "occlusive agent" which means it doesn't penetrate; instead it will sit on the skin to create a barrier that slows or blocks moisture evaporation. Silicone oils can be occlusive agents as well. The same type of moisture build-up would occur if you wrapped the skin in the plastic wraps that keep foods fresh in the refrigerator. Occluding the skin causes moisture build up, but we wouldn't think of these plastic wraps as a skin moisturizer, even though they increase the level of moisture in skin. Increased water content can also function to soften and improve skin flexibility and can also causing plumping. Of course, the same happens in the nail plate, but to a lesser degree and the reverse happens as well. Oils can also block penetration of excessive amounts water from the outside into nails, hair or skin and keep them from becoming over saturated with water molecules.

32:2 We have all heard that lemon juice help's flaking nails. To my knowledge lemon is acidic and acid corrodes, right? Is lemon juice good for nails?

Just because something is an acid, doesn't make it corrosive to the nail plate. Saliva is acid and so is vinegar, so not all acids will corrode. I don't think lemon juice is a useful treatment for nails and I'm unaware of any benefits. However, there is an unexpected problem with giving a lemon juice nail treatment. Lemon or lime juice can absorb into the surrounding skin and upon exposure to sunlight, small amounts chemically change into a new substance that can cause allergic skin reactions. Therefore, this is a risky treatment that I would recommend that nail professionals avoid. If lime or lemon juice contact the skin and are then exposed to the sun for more than fifteen minutes, this can lead to a highly visible, streaky rash on the skin that often lingers for several months. The worst of the rash lasts for two or three weeks. The medical term is for this skin reaction is "phytophotodermatitis". Phyto means plant- based, and photodermatitis refers to skin condition (dermatitis) related to light or UV exposure (photo). These skin reactions can look like burns or a rash on the skin that usually appears 36-72 hours after exposure to sunlight.

They can look like small reddish bumps and range all the way up to large blisters. In severe cases these reactions can even be nausea, vomiting, and fever associated with the rash. Citrus juices in small quantities as ingredients are fine, but I don't recommend using concentrated raw citrus juice of any type on the nail or surrounding skin. These are non-professional treatments and potentially risky for clients that get significant sun exposure after the treatment.

Special Topic - Risky Machine Manicures

Some are teaching a highly risky technique that goes by several different names including, the "Russian" or "Equipment" or "E-File" manicure. What it's called, doesn't matter, they are essentially the same. I believe these new methods are a potential threat to the entire nail industry. Here's why: these are procedures that can be "invasive" and they promote the intentional cutting and/or abrasion of the living skin sounding the nail plate. Those who teach these techniques don't use the term "abrasion", instead using nicer marketing terms like "buffing" or "polishing". Also, they claim to be removing pterygium, which would be incorrect to do. What they doing is removing skin from the proximal nail fold and side walls. They claimed the "nails look prettier", but in my view, this is a poor reason to jeopardize a client's health, when safer ways to perform a manicure exist.

Cutting/abrading will damage skin and create the very problem manicures are supposed to solve, more damaged skin that later must be cut or abraded away- like a dog chasing its own tail! Many report the skin around the nail plate grows back thicker, so they need to continue the method regularly, just to keep up. Nail salons are already under intense scrutiny and don't need the media or salon-bashing activist groups using this as another reason to avoid salons, which is a concern. Many will be frightened by such techniques, which will make more people frightened of nail technicians and their services, rather than to enjoy the many benefits that salons offer.

Some justify their actions claiming to use only sterile or disposable implements, naively believing this prevents infections. Wrong! Whenever the living skin is cut or abraded, the damaged area is more susceptible to infection for many hours, even days and will remain so until the damage heals. One proponent of these methods argued, "I've never heard of that happening." Of course not! Not many would openly admit they cut a client's skin and caused an infection. And schools and teachers who promote these methods don't check back with their students on a regular basis, so how could they know about when these methods are being misused? I've seen these types of infections occur many times. Also, when this thin skin is damaged, it becomes more susceptible to irritation and may lead to permanent allergic reactions to nail coating products. How? Many who use this technique place nail coating products directly onto or up against the damaged skin, further increasing the client's risk for adverse skin reactions. Some teachers say the bits are not abrasive and are smooth, but if they were not abrading the skin, then they would have no effect. These bits may be less abrasive, but when any bit is spinning at thousands of RPM and placed against the skin, the surface will be abraded. This abrasion can reduce the skin's effectiveness as a barrier, which makes it easier for infections and adverse skin reactions to occur.

Another person asked if it's such a risk, why are so many doing it? "*Fools Rush in where Angels Fear to Tread*", just because some do this, doesn't mean it's safe. This method should NOT be taught to the masses via Internet videos or via on-line classes. Yet this is what's being done and some are "jumping on the bandwagon", without considering the consequences to their clients or their business. Nor do I think so-called certification classes are the answer. Many students of these courses often disregard important precautions and will return to the salon and do it “their way”. Then they will teach other nail technicians “their way” and those nail technicians will also do it “their way”. Soon, the precautions will be forgotten and this could have unforeseen consequences that could harm clients and may be disastrous for the reputation of the nail industry. Interestingly, many who do these services claim they do it the safe way and others do not, but isn’t that the *“pot calling the kettle black”*? Besides, using an e-file to smooth this skin is considered microdermabrasion and in many regions is restricted only to those with special licenses beyond nail technician licensing. For instance, in the US an esthetician license (or sometimes a cosmetology license) is required to perform microdermabrasion.

I can walk on a rope that is one inch from the ground, and not get hurt if I fall, but if I try to walk on the same rope, five feet above the ground, I could get seriously injured. An expert rope walker wouldn’t worry about falling from five feet- they are experts. The low rope, allows a lot of room for error for non-experts, while the high rope allows “little room for error”. When high speed bits are used and manicures become motorized, this allows little room for error. The skin around the nails is nothing like that on the palm of the hand of bottom of the foot. It is much thinner and easier to damage. Bedsides, even calluses should not be filed smooth, since this also increases the risks of infections. A protective layer of callus should always be left behind. Some e-file experts understand how to prevent injuries, but this is not such an easy thing to teach to non-experts, especially after just a few hours of instruction (or even a few days), which is what most classes offer.

NEVER intentionally cut or abrade the skin around the nail plate- that’s trouble waiting to happen! NEVER place any nail coating product directly against the skin, especially damaged skin- this increases the risks of skin irritation and permanent allergies to these products- more trouble waiting to happen. Protect and pamper the skin around your client’s nails- don’t invade it. Explain to your clients and friends why they should avoid this as well.

Pedicure and Foot Related

6: Special Topic - How Can Pedicures be Safely Performed?

Pedicure services are a great value to clients, but many potential clients don't get salon pedicures. Many are concerned about news media reports concerning injury or infections from salon pedicures. Although this has increased awareness of the potential problems that can result from an improper service, the news media rarely mentions that pedicures, in general, are very safe when properly performed. Instead they present an extreme view, as if clients are taking a great risk. This is done to build drama and make their stories more interesting and scary. However, this is contrary to the facts! Many millions of pedicures are safely performed in the US each year without incident and many more are performed around the world. The clear majority of the time, salon pedicures are completely safe! However, infections and injuries do occur! When they do, this harms the entire salon industry. I've seen these infections and have served as scientific expert in court cases where this has occurred. I want to share what I've learned so that nail technicians can avoid these issues, because every time an injury or infection occurs, that's another black eye for salons everywhere. It's important for every salon professional to be aware of these issues and understand how to prevent them. This information is needed to maintain a healthy salon environment and provide a safe haven for clientele. Fortunately, this is easy to do, if you know how.

Pedicure chair, basin or bowl, they all require proper cleaning/disinfection. This must be done every time, between every client. If you use a disposable basin liner in your pedicure tub, be sure to dispose of them after every use and never reuse them. Products claiming they are anti-bacterial can't prevent biofilms or stop bacterial buildup on walls and other surfaces. What's a biofilm? When some bacteria congregate in high enough concentrations, they build a protective layer that acts like a nest where they can hide from disinfectants. This layer protects the bacteria, making them much harder to remove or destroy. An example of a biofilm is the sticky film that builds up inside your mouth overnight or if you don't brush daily. Using only mouth wash doesn't get rid of this film, just like rinsing or spraying won't remove biofilms from pedicure equipment. In fact, they are very difficult to remove without vigorous scrubbing with a clean and disinfected scrub brush. That's why the best way to deal with biofilms is to avoid letting them form in the first place. Cleaning and disinfecting pedicure equipment between each client prevents biofilm formation, which is why many government regulations related to salons require cleaning and disinfection of pedicure equipment before use on any client.

It is important to note that "anti-bacterial" salon products do NOT replace the need for cleaning and disinfection! Neither do the so-called "water sanitizers". Water sanitizers only treat the water, not the equipment. They cannot replace cleaning and disinfection. If used alone, these water sanitizers put clients at increased risk of infection. Before use on any client, nail professionals must properly clean/disinfect all pedicure tubs, bowls or basins that come into contact with the previous client's skin or the water used to perform their pedicure. Of course, the same is true for all disinfectable implements, tools, abrasives, etc. The Nail Manufacturer's Council on Safety (NMC) has many great informational brochures that discuss a wide range of nail salon related topics. You can find a brochure entitled, *"Pedicure Equipment Cleaning and Disinfecting Procedures"* on their website and it is published in English, Spanish, Korean, Russian, Vietnamese, www.Probeauty.org/NMC. This brochure outlines procedures that salons can use to protect clients from infection. The NMC is a part of the Professional Beauty Association and provides non-branded information that every salon professional can benefit from reading, so check out this website.

Injury and infection can occur from overly aggressive removal of calluses or cutting skin, which can lead to serious infections... even if you sterilize your implements! How can this happen? If the skin on a client's foot is injured and skin broken- infection will be possible until skin repairs itself! The skin is a barrier and when this barrier is breached, an infection becomes more likely. Clients could pick up an infection at home that evening walking on their own floor if the nail technician:

A. Removed too much callus

B. Injured living skin with file and/or pusher

C. Misused corrosive callus softeners/removers

Each of these can break the skin barrier, making infections more likely. Be very cautious while filing the nails to avoid cutting the skin. One way is to score new files by rubbing the edges of two nail files together to remove overly sharp edges. Another way is to avoid pushing back the living skin too aggressively. This can break the seals that protect the nail bed and matrix from infection. Calluses protect the feet from friction that can rub skin raw or puncture wounds of the skin. That's why it is important to only smooth down callus and not completely remove the natural protective barrier the skin has created for itself. The skin creates a callus for a reason, so don't remove them completely, even if a client insists. Explain to them that you are concerned for their safety.

Use callus products with great care, because most are corrosive to skin. That's how they work. They corrode (dissolve) skin and will do this even to healthy living skin and eyes. I recommend wearing protective gloves and safety eye wear to prevent skin/eye injury. These products can be seriously damaging to living tissue if they remain on the skin for too long or get into the eyes. They work by softening and slowly dissolving the hardened skin. So, keep these products away from healthy skin. Healthy skin is easier to dissolve than a callus and therefore can be damaged more quickly. If the foot isn't properly rinsed to remove all corrosive callus products, the residuals left on the foot can slowly damage living tissue. Therefore, be especially careful to remove all products from the foot, as well as from your hand/fingers. Also, be especially careful to rinse well between the toes and along the side walls of the nail plate. Never use corrosive callus products on the top of the foot. The skin is very thin at the top of foot, so damage can occur quickly. Don't put corrosive callus products into squirt bottles! These should be carefully applied, to keep them away from healthy skin. They should never be "applied liberally", instead apply them in a careful and controlled fashion.

Do not seal corrosive callus products to the skin with plastic wrap. This will accelerate the action of these corrosives on the callus, which is why some do this, but the plastic wrap will cause them to more quickly corrode healthy skin, as well. ***Avoid doing this!*** I recommend setting a timer so that you don't forget to remove the corrosive callus product as directed. I've seen serious accidents occur when nail professionals were distracted and forgot the client. Leaving these corrosive products on the skin for longer than recommended is very risky and should be avoided, which is why they should be used exactly as directed in the product instructions. Also, make sure to protect your own skin, by wearing protective gloves e.g. nitrile or vinyl. Never use a razor, sharp blades or knives to cut callus. This potentially harmful practice can remove too much callus and can accidentally slice the skin- which will significantly raise the client's risks of infection. I also do NOT recommend using lava or pumice rocks. These can be over aggressive, especially if callus softeners are used. Besides pumice stones have many cavities on their surface, which trap skin and other debris making them very difficult to properly clean and almost impossible to properly disinfect, so I don't recommend their use.

In short: smooth, don't remove calluses, clean and disinfect everything that comes into contact with the client's skin or pedicure water, carefully use gentle filing techniques to avoid accidental cuts. Professional pedicures are valuable and rewarding. To protect this business for the future, it is important that all nail professionals take these precautions seriously. Remember, when you protect your client's heath; you're also protecting the reputation of salons everywhere.

7: Special Topic - Update on Nail Fungus; New Scientific Information

While at the Orlando Beauty show, I ran into the well-known and highly respected podiatrist Dr. Robert Spaulding. I'm a scientist, not a medical professional which is why I don't speak much about medical diseases or treatments. For that, I rely on podiatrists and dermatologists to keep me updated about new information related to the medical field. At this event, I asked him what's new? As always, his reply was very interesting. He told me about new information concerning fungal infections of the nail plate and surrounding skin. Newer types of lab testing on infected nail plates are providing much more detailed information.

These lab reports provided dermatologists and podiatrists with a much more powerful way to find and identify infectious organisms on the nail plate. They can now identify organisms that could not have been identified by other methods. What does this mean? Medical professionals have a better diagnostic tool, so they can better find and understand nail infections.

I'll discuss some important aspects of fungal nail infections, but not for diagnosis or treatment purposes, that's best left to medical professionals. Instead the goal is to prevent these types of infections and understand what to do in case of an unhealthy condition that may be infectious.

The predominant types of fungal infections identified on the nail are called "dermatophytes". Dermatophytes are microscopic organisms that obtain their nutrients from keratin found in nails, skin and hair. When these infect the nail plate, they live and grow by digesting the nail plate. In other words, they eat keratin. This helps explain why the nail plate appears to thicken when infected by such pathogens (organisms that cause infections). The nail plate begins to fall apart and the layers of the nail plate separate, resulting in the nail plate appearing to thicken, when actually it's swelling apart. The nail isn't growing thicker, nor is the nail matrix making additional layers of nail cells. There are about one-hundred thousand types of known fungal organisms and probably many more that have not yet been identified. They are everywhere! One way they spread is by direct contact with infected skin, nails or hair. For example, in nails these organisms are transferred by contaminated nail files. There are many ways to transmit these types of infections, e.g. walking barefoot on public carpet or flooring.

Both yeast and molds are part of the family of fungi and both can be transmitted by salon services. Molds are a type of fungi that were previously considered not to be dermatophytes, meaning they cannot digest or use skin/keratin as food. This helps explain why medical professionals used to believe that molds were not likely to cause nail infections. They were considered to be plant pathogens that did not infect the nail or living tissue on the body.

In short molds were not considered to be nail pathogens because;

1. they could not be identified within the infected nail plate, and

2. because they don't eat keratin.

What has changed? New studies show that molds can live on the nail plate, even though they don't eat keratin or nail oils. This can happen in two ways. Studies demonstrate that molds may sometimes create "secondary" infections, when following an existing fungal infection. The existing infection is the primary or main infection and they open a pathway for molds. Interestingly, fungal organisms breaking down and digesting the keratin and molds can infect the same area and eat special proteins found between the nail cells; proteins that help cement the nail cells together. These proteins are exposed when fungal organisms cause a nail cell to break apart, which then allows molds to sometimes co-infect the nail plate. In other words, molds may co-exist with other types of fungal organisms and live by digesting other substances released when keratin begins to breakdown down the nail plate. Molds normally would not infect the nail plate, unless previously infected by fungal organisms.

Also, these new medical test methods are revealing that some types of molds can digest keratin. It's also known that certain yeast can infect the nail and digest keratin. Some experts claim that up to 50% of nails that are infected by the more standard fungal organisms are also co-infected by molds. Such co-infections are often more difficult to treat and don't respond as well to conventional medical therapy making them harder to cure.

Even so, it is not correct or proper to tell clients they have a mold, just as it is not proper to tell them they have a fungal or bacterial infection- Nail techs have no way to make these determinations or provide a diagnosis. To tell your client they have a fungus is considered "diagnosis of a medical condition" which is not proper nor legal in many countries. Only licensed, qualified medical professionals should be providing diagnosis or medical treatment. If a nail tech instructs a client to soak in any solution or apply a topical treatment of any kind to treat such medical conditions- they are now prescribing treatments- which is also not proper for nail technicians to do. Should the client's condition worsen, the nail tech could be considered responsible. In the event a client's condition ever worsens, they should be instructed to immediately seek medical advice and treatment, if required. Cases of suspected nail infection should be referred to a qualified medical professional.

There are many different types of infectious organisms. Since these different organisms often produce similar symptoms that often look the same, it is impossible to identify the type of infection simply by looking at it. Never attempt to diagnosis or treat any type of nail infection, instead ask the client to bring a written release from the medical professional saying they are not infectious and their feet/nails are healthy enough to perform a pedicure. This is not only to protect them and other clients; it also protects you and the salon's reputation. What's the best way to prevent transmission of infectious organisms in the salon? Here are some tips:

When it comes to pedicures, be sure to practice proper cleaning and disinfection between every client. Don't be fooled into thinking that anti-bacterial products or water sanitizers replace cleaning and disinfection. Dispose of disposable items- never reuse them. If you drop a file on the floor, do not use it. Throw away if disposable or clean and disinfect if disinfectable. Don't keep nail files in your pockets, store them in a clean, dry location. Never use a nail file on an active or visible nail infection, this just helps to spread the nail or skin infection to fingers or toes of other clients.

Avoid wearing shoes that are too small- this can lead to onycholysis of the big toe. Any type of nail trauma that leads to onycholysis, can also lead to nail infections. Infectious nail organism's gain access to the open space under the nail plate and can colonize fungal or bacterial organisms to create an infection. Overly aggressive filing of the nail plate can also create such nail trauma that leads to damage and/or infection. Avoid using a nail file to thin down nails that appear to have suddenly grown thicker, since this could indicate the nail plate has become infected. Instead, refer the client to a podiatrist or dermatologist to ensure the nail isn't infected. Avoid filing the nail plate with heavy grit abrasive or using too much downward pressure on the nail file, since this can create too much thinning and damage. Avoid wearing the same shoes two days in a row. Shoes get damp from wearing them and can take more than overnight to dry out. Wearing shoes that are always slightly damp encourages the growth of pathogens. Keep the feet dry and these microorganisms can't survive. Changing the socks once a day and/or using foot powders can help keep feet drier.

It's everyone's responsibility to safely perform pedicures and to work within the scope of a nail professionals training. So, don't take short cuts when it comes to cleaning and disinfection AND do NOT work beyond your training, be sure to send clients to seek medical evaluations if you suspect an infection.

4:1 Should nail technicians remove the callus from the foot?

No, complete removal of a callus from the foot is considered a medical procedure. Nail technicians are only allowed to perform cosmetic procedures and may not remove calluses, nor may they cut any living skin. Our feet aren't stupid. They create a callus to solve a problem and thus prevent infection. Calluses prevent blisters. It's ok to use an abrasive (not a sharp blade) to gently smooth them.

Even if a client specifically requests removal; refuse and explain, that this is for their safety. Serious infections can result and your clients could lose their foot, even if sterilized implements are used- infections can still occur after leaving the salon if too much callus is removed. When it comes to calluses, smooth them and don't remove them!

4: Myth Do water sanitizers replace the need to clean and disinfect anything that holds water for a client's pedicure?

Powders and tablets are "water sanitizers" much like those used in pools and hot tubs. They are not registered as foot spa "disinfectants" and don't clean or disinfect, they are never used to replace proper cleaning and disinfection. This could put clients at risk of infection! Also, client's feet should never be in water containing a disinfectant. Wear gloves when handling disinfectants, keep fingers or hands out of these solutions.

13:2 It's summer! That means more pedicures and more dry feet. Clients want their feet to be nice and supple for summer. Unfortunately, that is not the case. Does the sun dry our feet? Why do they get hard at the bottom sole? What should we suggest to clients when they want their feet to be supple and soft for summer? I've been told rubbing Vaseline and sleeping with socks helps. What are the facts?

The sun doesn't dry out feet, but it does encourage wearing sandals and going barefoot. So, in the summer we are more aware and concerned about the condition of the feet. However, more barefoot walking increases the thickness of the skin on the bottom of the foot. Also, avoid wearing any type of poorly-fitted shoes, since this also contributes to skin hardening. That hard layer of skin on the bottom of the foot is caused by the friction that's created when the skin rubs against other surfaces.

The skin thickens to protect itself from whatever it is rubbing against it. If this hardened skin is removed, the foot will rebuild this necessary protective layer. Filing off the callus can cause increased thickening of the layer to add increased protection for the foot. Filing off this skin is a bit like a dog chasing its own tail. This is why it is important not to remove this layer of skin. Clients may want smooth supple feet; however, they don't want open sores, blisters and infections that can result when too much of this hardened layer is removed. In my opinion, it is far better to use skin softeners rather than remove this protection. Vaseline is not a skin softener. Applying petroleum jelly to the feet seals the skin so that moisture builds up in the tissue, which makes the skin feel softer, temporarily. The effect wears off once the petroleum jelly is removed and the moisture content of the skin returns to normal, usually within a few hours.

My recommendation is to not completely remove calluses or over-thin the hardened tissue on the bottom of the feet since these are protective layers. Smoothed with mild abrasive scrub or foot file is ok, but this layer should not be completely removed, only smoothed to make them a little more cosmetically acceptable. I recommend using professional products specifically designed for softening feet. These are much more likely to produce significant and longer lasting conditioning, as well as softening.

15:1 A friend of mine has a great toe nail that is halfway separating from the nail bed from the free edge back. Now it's turned deep yellow. Her other toes seem to be ok, except the other great toe nail is uneven and a little wavy looking. How can she have normal nail growth again? Or did she damage her nails? She is a personal trainer and runs a lot. Can the type of shoe make a difference? She recently started using a new type of shoe.

This is a very common problem that many runners, walkers and others with an active life style don't understand. This ignorance may cause them to injure their feet. Even many who sell athletic shoes for a living don't seem to understand how much the foot can swell and lengthen, especially during moderate to intense exercise. I'm a long-distance walker and often walk ten miles or more. That's sixteen kilometers, so I'm walking for four hours, non-stop. My feet swell on these walks, I always buy shoes that are two full sizes bigger than what fits me well while standing in the shoe store.

When we run or walk long distances the foot can swell a full shoe size or more. The foot can also swell just from standing for long periods. By the time I finish a long walk, my big toe is just touching the inside of my shoes, my feet are now two sizes longer, but they will typically return to their normal size in a few hours. If I bought shoes that were only one size too big, then my big toes would be crammed up against the inside of the shoes. This puts excessive pressure on the nail plate; sometimes enough to break the hyponychium seal underneath the free edge and with continued pressure, this condition will only worsen. Eventually, this could lead to the nail plate becoming separated from the bed, a condition called onycholysis. There is a risk that this space, which sits directly over the nail bed, may become infected or the great toenail may fall off completely.

If the nail plate has turned a dark color as you've described, that can indicate an infection so I can understand your concern. I recommend refraining from treating this nail until it can be examined by a medical professional to determine if an infection is present. Assuming no permanent damage has occurred, once minor physical trauma delivered to the nail plate and any infection is eliminated, the plate may once more grow normally. Prolonged, repeated or severe physical trauma is often the cause. When you purchase shoes for any type of athletic use, including walking for more than an hour you should consider ensuring they are large enough to accommodate swelling. Check to ensure there is somewhere between a thumb and two fingers width of clear space between the end of the longest toe and the inside of the shoe which shoemakers call the "toe box". Wavy-looking lines across the width of the nail plate are another indicator. The nail plate is solid, but it can flow and change shape when exposed to constant pressure or repeated impact. The nail plate is deformable and these ripples are created in the nail plate when it repeatedly pushes against the inside of the toe box.

If this is ignored, the condition can eventually turn into onycholysis and may eventually become infected. Ask your friend to check her shoes size by gauging how much space is between the tip of the toe and the inside of the shoe. She should do this at the beginning, middle, end of a run, and three hours after the run. She'll be amazed at the changes in foot length. That is really pretty cool, if you think about it. The feet have a lot of flexibility and grow larger when we need them most and calm back down to get small. Remember, after strenuous exercising that involves the feet, it's a good idea to check your shoes to ensure they aren't pressing against your great toes. If the great toe nail is separating from the bed or largest toe nail plate is wavy or there are calluses on the tips of your toes, don't suspect your new shoes, instead suspect their size! Don't you just love feet? I know that I sure do. Make sure you take care of them. They need you, and you need them.

16:1 There are a couple of toenail reconstruction products on the professional market now that claim you can apply the product directly to the nail bed. These products have been used by podiatrists for years. Yet we've always been told never to let monomer or uncured gels near the skin, let alone the nail bed! Can you explain the contradiction?

There is no contradiction. Monomer and uncured UV gels should not be intentionally applied to the skin due to the potential for developing permanent allergy. This is a fact that has been twice confirmed by the prestigious Cosmetic Ingredient Review Expert Panel, aka CIR. I agree with the CIR and I don't condone use of such products by nail professionals when intentional skin application is the goal. This should not be done. I understand that some clients may want you to perform these services, but that's not a very good reason for performing any service that goes beyond the scope of nail salon services. As far as I know, very few podiatrists perform these services. Companies that market such products are attempting to convince more podiatrists to perform these services.

In fact, it is not very common at all among podiatrists. Prosthetic nails are sometimes used to replace seriously damaged or diseased nails that have been intentionally removed or permanently lost due to a medical condition or accident. Some types of prosthetic nails are based on materials that are different than those used by nail professionals, but there are a few that are based on the same types of ingredients. Even so, this type of work is outside the scope of nail technician's services and those who perform such services are taking a risk for themselves and their clients. If something goes wrong and the client is injured because of these services, the salon and nail tech will have a lot of difficult explaining to do. If this type of work is performed in a region that has professional licensing, more than likely the nail professional will run the risk of losing their license should the authorities receive complaints.

Clearly, direct skin contact with artificial nail products can and does cause adverse skin reactions in sensitive individuals. You can't always tell, and the longer a person wears a prosthetic nail of this type, the more likely it becomes they will develop an adverse skin reaction. That's how it works. Adverse skin reactions are caused by prolonged and/or repeated contact- over time. It could take months, maybe years for permanent allergies to develop. Don't let this happen to you. Avoid working on unhealthy nails and always avoid skin contact with artificial nail coatings of all types. In short, I do NOT recommend these types of prosthetic services. Instead, I recommend that nail professionals only service healthy and intact nails and skin.

17:2 While working with older people doing their pedicure, I find that some nails are bent sharply inward at the free edge. This is uncomfortable and sometimes causes pain. Why does the nail plate take on this shape?

This demonstrates how important the finger and toe bones are when it comes to shaping the nail plate. As we age the bones that make up the tip of the toe begin to slowly breakdown. These bones are called phalanges (pha-lan-gees) or one of these bones is called a phalanx (fal-angks). As this occurs, the underlying supporting base for the nail plate grows smaller. This causes the nail matrix to change shape and become more highly curved. Since the curvature of the nail matrix determines the curvature of the nail plate as the matrix curls into a tighter curvature, the nail plate adopts the same tight curvature, as you described. These are aptly named "Pincer nails". Another common reason this occurs is from wearing ill-fitted shoes. This can happen on both toes and fingers, but frequently occurs on the toe nails and is relatively rare on finger nails. When pincer nails occur on the hands, it's sometimes related to the breakdown of bone due to osteoarthritis.

Pincer nails can also occur in younger people and there are different types. For instance, hereditary pincer nails that "run in the family" are almost always symmetrical in shape, meaning equally balanced curvature on each side of the nail. The great toes are most affected, but other toes can be as well. Pincer nails that are acquired later in life are often not symmetrically shaped, meaning that they have different degrees of curvature on each side of the nail plate. Acquired pincer nails can be a result of disease conditions such as psoriasis, cysts, tumors or even a fungal infection. If the surrounding skin becomes red and feels unusually warm or tender, the nail should be examined by a podiatrist or other qualified medical professional. Several medical treatments have been devised for conditions that are deemed to be extreme enough to warrant treatment. Doctors may use surgical treatments to correct this condition, however there are more conservative treatments for lesser conditions. Clients with such problems should be referred to a qualified medical professional.

23:1 When I was in Europe, I had a fish pedicure. I started wondering if these are safe? I've heard they can transmit disease. Is there any truth to this?

Pedicures using the so-called "doctor fish" to nibble dead tissue from the feet were originally practiced in the Middle East since these fish normally live in warm water springs found in this region. Then this practice spread to Southeast Asia and from there was imported to Europe, the US, Canada, Australia and other places. Many regions have banned fish pedicures, and for good reason. There are several important reasons why this practice is unwise and potentially unsafe. To protect clients from infections, everything that comes in contact the previous client's skin should be cleaned and disinfected. That can't occur with these so-called "Fish Pedicures". These fish can't be cleaned nor can they be disinfected. I recently visited two such salons, one in London and the other in Copenhagen.

I watched as one client left, another quickly took their place. I didn't see any equipment being cleaned or disinfected. In fact, they used the same water for both clients. I watched for a while and saw this repeated again and again. I asked about this at the London spa and they told me they sterilized the fish and the water, but I explained to them this wasn't possible. Even if the water were exposed to UV, as they claimed, clearly the fish can't be sterilized; they would die in the process. Also, UV water treatments have several disadvantages; the main one is that these systems use UV-C energy which is harmful to skin. UV-C lamps must be shielded from skin and can't be placed in the tub where the feet are located so the actual container where the feet are placed is not sterilized nor did I see it being disinfected; only the water is treated. Both salons did appear to have pretty blue lights placed inside the tanks with the feet, but these could NOT have been UV-C bulbs. Instead these are just decorative lighting that would have no effect on the condition, cleanliness or quality of the water. Instead, their only benefit would be to make the clients feel safer. I looked on the Internet and researched several of the water and tank systems sold to salons for this purpose.

The sellers of these UV-C water treatment systems for fish pedicures promoted the impressive lighting inside the tanks which leads me to believe the blue light is intended to fool the consumers. When I watched these services performed in these salons, as I mentioned previously I didn't see these foot baths being cleaned and disinfected between clients, nor do I believe this is regularly done. Since the fish would have to be removed, the tank drained and scrubbed, then filled with a disinfection solution, such as chlorine bleach and would require soaked for ten minutes to ensure complete disinfection and then the tank would have to be rinsed to remove the residual disinfectant and refilled. Some systems sold for this use contained many hundreds of gallons of water and are designed to provide services for many people to use at one time. Obviously, the water in these pools are not likely to be changed regularly either.

Another problem is that the fish excrement contains bacteria which can serve as food for further bacterial growth, and this goes into the water along with the client's feet. But the biggest issue in my view is that there is no way around the fact that these foot baths MUST be scrubbed cleaned and disinfected between each client. What's the harm if this isn't done? The problem is that a biofilm can build up on the container walls and inside water pipes that are not directly exposed to the UV-C.

What is a biofilm? An example of a biofilm is found on your teeth when you wake up in the morning. Biofilms serve as a breeding ground for bacteria and form quickly overnight while you sleep. Just rinsing your mouth with clean water won't remove these sticky films, nor will rinsing with mouthwash. The teeth need vigorous brushing to remove this biofilm and brushing is the only way to dislodge and remove the bacteria that create such films. Bacteria live inside these sticky biofilms and they serve as a protective nest that allows the bacteria to hide from disinfectant solutions. Biofilms can't hide bacteria from direct exposure to UV-C exposure, if the foot tub and all piping are not directly exposed to UV-C and regularly cleaned, biofilms will build up and can present an infection risk to clients. When I explained this to the person at the front desk, she just shrugged and said, "Then don't have one". I took her good advice and left the salon. But wait, there's more. I did notice a false claim on a website selling these fish to salons and spas that I want to comment about. The website claimed these fish can't carry diseases.

A 2012 study published in a scientific journal called *Emerging Infectious Disease* which is published by the prestigious US Center for Disease Control pointed out these fish can and have carried disease causing organisms which may cause infections in people. This paper explained that 6000 fish imported to England from Indonesia for use in salons were affected by a bacterial disease that caused them to bleed from their gills, mouths and stomachs. Nearly all the fish died as a result. The researchers followed up by testing five more batches of imported fish headed for London salons, they discovered many other fish were also infected by other disease causing pathogens that turned out to be resistant to many common antibiotics. To my knowledge, there have been only a few reported salon infections related to disease carried by these fish so that doesn't appear to be a very big problem, but it can occur in some rare instances.

Also, I want to make it clear that it is not at all likely that a virus could be spread in this way, so there is no concern that HIV infections would be transmitted in this fashion, as some have incorrectly reported. In fact, HIV is extremely unlikely to be transmitted by any type of pedicure and to my knowledge this has never occurred. Some have argued with me over the years saying, "Well it could happen." Well... a giant meteorite "could" hit the salon while I was having a pedicure, but that's not going to stop me from getting pedicures. "Can" and "will" are two very different things. **Beware**. The words "can" or "could" are often used to trick people into thinking highly unlikely things are likely to occur. Often this trick is used to sell a product or service that a person would normally not purchase unless they were frightened into doing so. Watch for this type of deceptive practice. It is often used by fear-based activist groups and fear-based marketers. Anyone suggesting that HIV could be spread by salon pedicures is ignoring that the odds are probably greater than at least one in five billion, since at least that many salon pedicures have been performed since HIV was discovered in the early 1980s.

What's my biggest concern with fish pedicures? It is only this, proper cleaning and disinfection of the tools and equipment is the very best way to prevent infections and the water should always be changed between clients, but the way fish pedicures are performed prevents this from being done properly. After reviewing all available information, my advice would be to not have or give fish pedicures. I don't see how these important and necessary steps can be done properly when live fish are involved and that is my biggest concern and why I recommend against them. On the topic of pedicures in general, I'd like to address one other myth. There are *no* additives that can be placed into the water with the client's feet that will replace the need to properly clean and disinfect the pedicure basin between each client.

Water sanitizing tablets or powders only treat the water and will not clean or disinfect the foot tub, nor will they remove or prevent biofilms. These tablets and powders should never be relied upon as replacement for proper cleaning and disinfection, just as UV-C water treatment systems are not a replacement for proper cleaning and disinfection. These can only treat the water, and can NOT disinfect or sterilize the equipment. In short, none of these are effective replacements and they will not protect clients. I do believe disposable pedicure liners are a great option and I support their use in salons. Even if you use one, the liner and the water must be disposed of each time and anything that comes in contact with the client's skin must be cleaned and disinfected to prevent the spread of transmittable infections. It is the responsibility of all salon professionals to ensure this is done, every time.

32:1 I have been hearing a lot about ionic/detoxifying foot baths lately, and I was wondering if you could give me your opinion about them? Do they really work? I find it hard to believe that toxins can be removed in this way.

So-called foot spa detox machines have been sold under a variety of brand names for many years. I've purchased and tested them and in my opinion these devices and their claims are fraudulent. This is nothing more than a marketing scam to fool people who don't understand how they really work. The sellers of these devices show pictures of water that changes color when the feet are soaked, claiming the color is due to "toxic matter" in the body coming out through your feet. This is a hoax. Toxins can't be drawn through the feet and all that is really being shown is a chemical trick. The sellers instruct that salt be added to the water. This is done to increase the conductivity of the water, so that small amounts of electrical current can be transmitted between two electrodes. This starts a process called "electrolysis", which is similar to how batteries work. The electrical current causes the electrodes to begin to corrode. This corrosion process dissolves small amounts of the electrode into the water, which is why these metal electrodes must be replaced from time to time. The electrodes are iron or copper based. As they corrode into the water, they react with oils, lotions, nail polish, soap residues, bacteria, clothing fibers, fungi or whatever happens to be on the surface of the skin, toenails or in the water. This causes a chemical reaction that creates new iron or copper compounds which add color to the water. Some of these new compounds aren't soluble in water, so they form colored solids which settle to the bottom of the container. Scientifically, these claims are the purest of nonsense and there is no proof to what they claim.

In fact, I've read reports from studies that have looked for body toxins in the colored water and found none. They do find lots of iron sulfate, which is naturally a brown or reddish-brown color. Also, dissolved copper reacts in the salt water to create a brownish solid. Depending on what else is in the water, you can see orange, green, black flecks (iron oxides), etc. You don't even have to put your feet in the water, and it will change color. I put in USDA certified; organically grown strawberries and the water color changed to brown. In my opinion, these devices do nothing positive for the user and are a complete waste of money. The same is true for the pads that are put on the bottom of the feet to draw out toxins; this is quackery, not science or medicine. No significant amounts of toxins are removed through the feet and none are found in the water when it is analyzed. There are other variations on this scam that use herbs or essential oils to pull out the toxins, but it's all trickery, so my advice is to save your money and get a pedicure instead.

Image 13: USDA Organic Strawberries in tap water BEFORE treatment and AFTER treatment.

Ingredients

12: Special Topic - Parabens and Other Preservatives

My best friend is a breast cancer survivor and I'm happy to say she is completely cured. Fortunately, there are more and more survivors like her each year. Breast cancer rates appear to have leveled off and the survival rate is improving each year. This is all good news in my book. More and more is being learned about this terrible disease and I believe we will someday soon be able to prevent and eliminate breast cancer.

Why am I telling you all of this? Recently, I went with my friend for her yearly checkup. I was more than a bit surprised to hear the doctor tell her that because of her past breast cancer, it was important that she should avoid parabens. She was "supposedly" extra susceptible to them. Well, I hadn't said very much, until then. I kept a calm straight faced and asked, "Excuse me Doctor, where did you get this information?"

He explained he had read it on an environmental group website that talked about the dangers of cosmetics. I then asked, "How do you know their information is correct?"

He stammered a bit, before finally admitting he had no way of knowing if this information was true, but he did claim to have read it "somewhere else before" on an Internet website about the supposed dangers of parabens. I know the feeling, we read so much, that sometimes we're not sure where we read something or why we believe it is correct. In other words, he was just parroting/repeating what he read and believing the information without asking any questions, even though no convincing evidence at all was provided or offered. This doctor knew almost nothing about the subject other than what he had read on these two websites. Yet, he's been telling this to patients ever since as if it were proven fact and they likely believed every word he said, but none of it was correct. Yes, doctors are busy people too and they make mistakes like everyone else, including me. Most people probably expect that doctors would do some fair and unbiased research before immediately jumping to a conclusion, apparently not, at least in this case.

I hear this question all the time, "who has the time to do any research?" However, the real question is- what are the consequences if you don't? How else can you ensure that your facts are correct or that you are not being duped? I've experienced this myself, so I know how easy it is to happen. So, if this can happen to me, it can happen to you. Not only is it wise to do some research, but you should always question the source and never automatically believe what you read or hear. Be a little skeptical about what you see on TV or the Internet, etc. That's a good thing to be, skeptical. Avoid the trap that many fall into, don't just look for information that supports what you want to believe. Instead, seek the truth even if it disagrees with your most cherished beliefs or notions. So, allow me to add the following to your research on the subject of parabens and preservatives. Here is some information I hope you will consider:

Fear-based activist groups needlessly frighten people claiming that "parabens" cause breast cancer. What? No way, not the ones used in cosmetics. The original claim was based on surprisingly weak evidence! In fact, the claim was largely based on ONE poorly performed and very small scientific study. That study has since been completely discredited by other researchers performing follow up studies. It has now been determined that these original claims were bogus. Worse, in my opinion, the author manipulated the results so she could pretend to have made a big and important discovery. In other words, she wasn't seeking the truth; she was seeking to prove what she wanted to believe. That's always risky business for anyone, especially scientific researchers. There are many, many types of parabens and only a few are used in cosmetics. It is nonsense to say that commonly used parabens in cosmetics are harmful, but lazy deceivers paint all parabens with one brush. Cosmetic parabens are among the safest preservatives for cosmetics and it is a down-right shame that deceivers have tricked the public into thinking they are harmful, when in fact they increase the safety of cosmetics by controlling the growth of bacteria, fungi and yeasts better than other preservatives. Parabens are also much less likely to cause skin sensitivity when compared to other preservatives.

At last, a well-known voice in the breast cancer community is speaking out against this misinformation by providing the real facts. The well-known breast cancer non-profit organization, the Susan G. Komen Foundation, released a press release from which I will quote some pertinent passages:

"Parabens have been linked to breast cancer because a small study in 2004 found parabens in breast cancer cells. However, the study did not consider other factors that could have led to the presence of parabens in the cells. Since this study, there have been many discoveries about parabens and breast cancer. Although parabens have some weak estrogen-like activity, they do not appear to build up in the tissue from cosmetic use and they have not been found to cause cancer in animals and parabens are not considered a health risk at this time".

Which is just a nice way of saying the original study was silly and cannot be believed and after years of studying parabens, we can confirm they are not a cause of breast cancer and are not a health risk. I'm very happy the Komen Foundation is recognizing what occurred, the researcher making these erroneous claims never bothered to compare the breast cancer tissue to normal breast tissue. Had she done so, this would have demonstrated that her assumptions were incorrect. Instead, she chose to automatically assume the traces of parabens found in the tissue must be the cause of the breast cancer and without any real proof.

In my view, this is more than a just a silly mistake, this is scientific incompetence. This researcher seems to have been more interested in proving what she already believed was true, rather than seeking out the truth. That's not real science; that's called junk science. Junk science is fake science. Unfortunately, the use of phony, junk science is becoming all too common with many cosmetic activist groups. These groups don't care about the facts, when they disagree with their preconceived notions and misguided beliefs. They'd much rather rely on Junk Science! These groups will sponsor bogus studies and pretend they're valid scientific studies. These so-called studies are nothing more than a game of charades designed to fool the public, news media and politicians. That's why for years I've asked people to not listen to fear-based activist groups, never donate money to them, and don't use their websites. They'll just use the donated money to unfairly attack cosmetics and continue to needlessly frighten the public with junk science and more trickery. Why does this matter?

Parabens are very important preservatives that are highly effective in a wide range of cosmetics. They prevent the growth of a wider range of microbes than most preservatives. Not only are they among the most useful preservatives, they are likely among the safest. They are highly effective against bacteria, fungi and yeast even at low concentrations and are much less likely to cause adverse skin reactions. Some other preservatives don't work unless you add more than 5 times as much. It a terrible shame to see how fear-based activism has gone so horribly wrong and how much damage they have unfairly caused by their distortions, but that is what they do. In the name of activism, these tricksters attack whatever they don't like for any reason and say whatever they want without any real evidence or proof, and no one holds them accountable for these intentional deceits.

Now you can understand why you'll rarely see these fear-based groups debate scientists like myself. They know the facts will expose them and they fear the truth. You would too if you made your living by distorting information to create unfounded fear and anxiety. They do this to your clients, alarming them needlessly and collecting millions in donations to help fund their misguided causes. It's not fair and it harms the entire cosmetic and beauty industry. Unfortunately, this has led to some poorly preserved products with shorter shelf lives and a greater risk of contamination. That's a real risk, this can harm people!

Make no mistake- preservatives are necessary for safety in food, drugs and cosmetics. Anyone who says otherwise doesn't understand the facts. Preservatives help ensure product safety and improve our quality of life. Don't let these tricksters fool you and make sure you inform your clients about this issue, as well. Help spread the truth and stop this nonsense before it causes any more unnecessary damage. Tell your clients to not listen to these fear-mongers and NEVER donate money to them. If you want the facts about cosmetic ingredients, you won't get them from these fear-based websites. You'll just get more fear, accompanied by a request for your monetary donations. Instead, I'll recommend two sites that provide fact-based information;

http://www.cosmeticsinfo.org and
http://personalcaretruth.com/

I've contributed information to both sites and have reviewed what they provide, so I can vouch for them. These websites provide up-to-date, fact-based information about cosmetic ingredients and I highly recommend them, so please have a look.

17:1 Have formaldehyde levels been found to be unsafe in nail salons?

No, formaldehyde is not a problem in nail salons and never has been. The so-called risk of formaldehyde in nail polish campaign was designed to mislead consumers, not to inform them. Here's why I say this; a multi-year independent scientific study was performed under the guidance of the California State Attorney General with the goal of measuring formaldehyde gas levels in salons.

Many sizes and types of salons were tested in both Northern and Southern California and during the winter and summer, which is why it took more than a year to complete. The study demonstrated conclusively that formaldehyde levels in nail salons are no different than what would be expected in other common workplaces where nail products were not in use. Interestingly, during the study it was observed that the formaldehyde levels were highest in the morning when the salon first opened and then dropped off steadily throughout the morning, leveling off at their normally low levels in the afternoon. Why? When the salon was closed for the night, traces of formaldehyde gas can build up as they normally do in closed spaces. Traces slowly escape from carpet glue and building material, e.g. plywood. When a salon is opened and the air begins to circulate, the formaldehyde levels drop back down to normal levels. Even so, all the measured air concentrations in the nail salon study were considered safe.

When the study was concluded and the final report was issued, the California governmental authorities ruled that based on extensive salon exposure data, any levels of formaldehyde in salon from nail polish, treatments, and hardeners were SO LOW THAT NO CONSUMER WARNINGS ARE REQUIRED. In other words, nail polish does NOT release formaldehyde gas into the air to create any health risk whatsoever, even under what is probably the most stringent formaldehyde regulation in the world. This is because nail polish has never contained formaldehyde gas as an ingredient. Fear-based advocacy groups have tricked consumers into thinking that it does, but it's just a big deception intended to frighten your friends, family and customers to get them to donate money. Any gases in nail polish could only exist in very tiny traces and would be dissolved in solvent solutions, e.g. 0.0001% or a ten thousandth of a percent! Some confuse a hard polymer resin called tosylamide formaldehyde resin, thinking this solid polymer is the same as formaldehyde gas... it's not even close. It can be a source of the traces of formaldehyde dissolved in solution, but these are very safe levels and will not cause harm. Some claim these are dangerous because they release formaldehyde, well so do people. We naturally exhale traces of formaldehyde in our breath, because our bodies naturally make and use formaldehyde on a daily basis, so clearly many are exaggerating the risks.

Some nail hardeners contain "methylene glycol" at around 1-2%. In the past manufacturers were required to call this ingredient by the incorrect name, "formaldehyde" rather that it's correct name, "methylene glycol". This error has since been corrected, but it's probably where the confusion began, and what caused these fear-based advocacy groups to incorrectly claim that nail polish contained dangerous amounts of formaldehyde. But even when I told them of their error and provided them with proper information, these groups continued to ignore the facts and provide misinformation.

Their tricky distortions were clearly intended to frighten the public and to encourage donations to help them force manufacturers to "stop selling carcinogenic nail polish." What silliness! These misguided groups claimed that up to 5% formaldehyde was used in nail polish, which was another huge distortion of the facts. When methylene glycol is used as a nail hardener, usually 2% or less, the container will typically contain less than 0.001% dissolved formaldehyde gas, not nearly enough to cause any harm to anyone. Even if all the formaldehyde suddenly came out at once, it still wouldn't be harmful. Why? Consider this; you naturally exhale formaldehyde with every breath. Even baby breath naturally contains traces of formaldehyde gas. Our bodies make formaldehyde regularly and use it to build substances such as proteins. Yes, formaldehyde is a naturally occurring, organic substance that's normally found even in unpolluted, pristine mountain air and in some organically grown foods such as apples. So, these groups have not provided all the facts and clearly there are safe levels of formaldehyde.

Formaldehyde is not the terrible boogieman these irresponsible groups claim it to be when they say there are no safe levels of formaldehyde. But why would they say this? Are they that clueless or just that tricky? Or is it both? Also, formaldehyde does not absorb through the skin or nails, as is wrongfully claimed by some.

It's only a potential inhalation risk and then only when exposure is to relatively high concentrations and over long periods; concentrations that would not be reached in a nail salon- certainly not from using nail polish! Formaldehyde can be irritating to skin, but so is my wool sweater. That doesn't make wool dangerous. It can also be irritating to the eyes, nose and throat, but not at levels found in the typical nail salon. Clearly, nail professionals are not exposed to any significant amounts of formaldehyde gas, nor is there any risk of harm from the tiny traces of formaldehyde found in salons or nail polish. An example of someone who should be concerned and would regularly monitor their breathing air to ensure they are not overexposed would be a factory worker in a place where formaldehyde is produced or used in the production of other substances- not nail salons or from using nail polish as has been falsely claimed.

Nail salons do not have to worry about monitoring the salon or working nail technicians for formaldehyde levels or exposure, since this is not a likely risk. In short, don't believe these anti-cosmetic fear groups! The make a lot of money scaring people and duping the media. Don't buy into their paranoia and misleading information. Formaldehyde is not a risk in nail polish and never has been. Nail polish is safe and has been for more than 80 years, which would explain why doctors and hospitals are not treating people harmed by using nail polish.

19:1 I started a discussion on my Facebook page a few weeks ago, that exploded into controversy. The topic that started this controversy… "Essential oils". Should they be ingested and are they safe for skin contact?"

I know there are plenty of myths and misinformation about essential oils, but I underestimated the passion of those who defend some of these myths. Don't get me wrong, I love essential oils. I was a very early adopter of the use of essential oils in the products that I've developed for use in salons and spas, as well as for retail use products. I'm fascinated by their composition, properties and great potential. But until recently I was not fully aware that so many have begun to ingest these oils for their so-called "therapeutic" benefits. Scanning the Internet, I was surprised that so many were promoting the ingestion of essential oils, usually to cure a medical ailment or as a preventative of a disease or disorder. Even more bothersome was that many people were being encouraged and assisted with self-diagnosis of their own medical conditions and encouraged to treat their disorders by ingesting essential oils.

As a scientist in the cosmetic, beauty and personal care industry, I am concerned about the lack of proper safety information and precautions, when it comes to ingesting essential oils. Why? First, aromatherapy oils are cosmetics and are NOT foods so they should not be "intentionally" ingested. Even those who claimed to be properly trained admit the practice of ingesting essential oils can be potentially dangerous without the proper training. You wouldn't know that by reading what's posted on the Internet by those who are promoting essential oils and suggesting improvements or cures for many conditions, aliments, and disorders. Those who are trained and only use the "therapeutic grade" essential oils claiming to be safe for internal use will say that essential oils not labeled as therapeutic may be unsafe to ingest. It seems to me like just about everyone is expressing some type of concern about the safety of this practice... including me.

Here are the problems and future challenges as I see them. There is NO generally recognized non-manufacturer body or group that certifies essential oils as therapeutic grade. That's not to say there is no such thing as "therapeutic grade", there clearly is, but that's not what it may appear to be. Some seem to mistake this as a regulatory quality standard and it is not. My concern is that many assume "therapeutic grade" infers that its medical grade or even government approved, and neither is correct to believe. As far as I can tell, these therapeutic standards are derived by the company selling the essential oils. That's a step in the right direction, but to ensure these standards are insulated sufficiently from undo marketing and sales influence, independent standards should be developed. Those standards should be fact-based and rely on valid scientific methods.

It's a myth that essential oils are chemical-free. Make no mistake, all essential oils are 100% chemical, however so are vitamin supplements and baby's breath. That's no surprise, if you know what a chemical is. ***A chemical is everything you can see or touch, except light and electricity.*** An essential oil commonly contains great numbers of different chemical components. By some estimates, at least 3000 different unique chemical substances have been identified as components of essential oils. Typical essential oils contain a few main chemical substances in high percentage that account for the fragrance and viscosity or thickness of that oil. The color of the essential oils is often caused by darkly colored, dissolved substances occurring in much lower concentrations within the oil. For many reasons, the ratios of these many components can vary widely, which means the chemical makeup of essential oils can vary greatly.

The essential oil's final composition depends on the type of plant, as well as the part of the plant used, the location where it was grown, the season it was harvested, the age of the plant when harvested and the local environmental conditions, as well as how the essential oil is removed from the plant, processed and stored. Essential oils are sometimes adulterated with other lower costing essential oils which often are unnoticeable without laboratory testing. As you can see, the chemical composition of an essential oil can vary widely and it depends on many various factors. This should help to explain why it is import to trace the essential oils from their source and to do laboratory testing to confirm its chemical composition and safety.

These aren't my main concern. My biggest concern is that some are known to be toxic by ingestion, yet people drink them, sometimes unaware of the potential for harm. Some essential oils are very irritating and are known to cause allergic reactions with prolonged and/or repeated exposures. This is one reason why many essential oils need to be greatly diluted before they are applied to the skin or else overexposure becomes a real possibility.

Even a drop or two in your water each day can be a problem, so don't kid yourself. Experts on both sides of the discussion agree that ingesting essential oils does affect the bacteria lining in your digestive tract. No one yet understands how, but there are many who are concerned that excessive exposure can lead to a range of gastrointestinal and digestive issues. In my opinion, too many are focused on the supposed benefits of ingesting essential oils and ignoring the potential for problems. These can't be forgotten. For example, some essential oils have strong antibacterial properties. What's the down side of ingesting these? Well, they could kill off large amounts of the bacteria that normally reside inside the stomach and line the intestine. Even though there are several pounds of bacteria lining these areas, ingesting these essential oils can throw off the normal balance and cause intestinal health problems.

Some think they are dismissing this argument by claiming essential oils only kill harmful bacteria, not the beneficial ones. Really? They can tell? Interestingly, there doesn't appear to be any scientific support for this claim. In my view, it is just wishful thinking based on speculation. Even then, I don't see how that argument helps their case at all, in fact it's a reason for concern. Isn't that the definition of an antibiotic? If it is true and some essential oils kill harmful bacteria in the gut, this would mean that some essential oils act like antibiotics when ingested. Therefore, long term ingestion should certainly be of concern, for that reason alone. Before essential oils are ingested there needs to be more research into this area.

It is important to note that the Alliance of International Aroma therapists have this to say on the matter, *"AIA does not endorse internal therapeutic use of essential oils unless recommended by a health care practitioner trained at an appropriate clinical level."* As far as other uses, I do NOT recommend that you apply undiluted, pure essential oils to skin. I recommend only using essential oils that are diluted in a carrier oil or other solvent. Essential oils can cause adverse skin reactions, which is why they should be greatly diluted.

There are two main myths I've heard,

1. It is erroneously said that essential oils contain no proteins so therefore for they must not be the cause of skin allergies, so the skin is just "detoxing".

    a. False, there are many well documented medical cases of allergic skin reactions to essential oils. Also, nickel is a common allergy causing substance and it contains no proteins. This myth is just plain false and deceptive.

    b. False, some claim that a rash or burning sensation of the skin when essential oils are applied is just your body detoxing. These symptoms are typical of skin irritation and/or allergic reactions and not the result of some imagined detoxification process. This is a silly attempt to come up with a positive explanation for any adverse skin reactions that any natural product might cause.

Sadly, many look for ways to avoid the facts and truths. It is important to understand that skin allergies are our bodies' natural reaction to natural substances. That's how our bodies work. These reactions are a skin protection mechanism that is triggered by exposure to natural substances. This is important to understand about your body; our skin develops allergic reactions as protection from natural substances that could injure or damage it if there were prolonged or repeated contact. The US Food and Drug Administration (FDA) discusses this potential problem on its website. Here is one such example, *"Allergic reactions have been reported with tea tree oil when taken by mouth or used on the skin. Skin reactions ranged from mild contact dermatitis (skin inflammation) to severe blistering rashes. Tea tree oil may cause bad breath, bad taste, depressed behavior, diarrhea, drowsiness, ear damage, fatigue, inflammation of the mouth, muscle tremors, nausea, and skin irritation (Burning, drying, eczema, fluid build-up, itching, rash, redness, scaling, warmth, and toxicity in human skin cells), slow or unsteady movements, stomach pain, uncommon blood changes, and weakness. Use cautiously in pregnant and breastfeeding women or those undergoing childbirth, due to reports that tea tree oil decreases contraction strength. Use cautiously when applied to the skin or when used as an eyelid scrub."*

Most chemicals have both a safe and unsafe level of exposure. That's also true of essential oils. This is a fact...many essential oils are more likely to cause adverse skin reactions when used in an undiluted form, i.e. 100% pure. You should understand that the more "pure" the essential oil, the "greater" the risk is because this means the concentration of the ingredients in the essential oils may be too high for safe skin exposure, so over exposure occurs. In general, over exposure causes adverse skin reactions. Pure, undiluted essential oils should NOT be applied to the skin. I raised this as a question on my Facebook page and after that discussion, someone who I will simply refer to as a "true believer" in ingesting essential oils was nice enough to call me to share her views on this subject.

She explained that essential oils are natural and therefore safe. Also, if the essential oil is 100% pure, it will be toxin free. She felt this was important because only pure and natural substances can remove synthetic toxins from the body. She was surprised when I told her that just about everything she believed about these oils was NOT correct. Many are confused by words like "toxin" or "natural", largely because they only listen to the "marketing" of these words and don't understand what these words truly mean. Why should you know the proper meaning? It becomes much easier to spot misinformation or deception. For instance, a "toxin" is a poisonous substance that is produced by a living organism, e.g. bee sting toxin or snake venom. That means ALL toxins are natural. If it's not natural, it's not a toxin. Yes, some synthetic materials may be "toxic" if overexposure occurs, that's different and not what I mean. They are NOT considered "toxins", but instead are called "synthetic toxicants".

What's my point? The word "toxin" only applies to naturally derived substances that can be poisonous to people. There are a lot of toxins and the list is really long. This should serve to remind us of the truth about nature. "Natural" doesn't mean automatically safe as some suggest. Nature is a very dangerous place filled with many types of naturally occurring poisons, toxins, allergens and other health hazards. Nature is not the LaLa-land we like to imagine it is. We do this because we don't have to actually live IN nature anymore and many don't visit it very often either, so most tend to forget the many risks and dangers that nature presents.

Of course, I will remain open minded on this subject and if new information develops, I will consider it, but for now, I'm in agreement with the Alliance of International Aromatherapists and I do not endorse internal therapeutic use of essential oils unless recommended by a medical doctor or other health care practitioner trained at an appropriate clinical level and only with judicious and cautious use. If I may give some closing advice, "clinical level" training is very comprehensive and not something that could be accomplished in a course lasting a few days, so don't be fooled.

20:3 What can you tell me about acetone? Does it affect the natural nail and does it harm it in any way? I'm hoping you can help shed light on this endless internet debate.

There are many related questions here; I'll try to address them all. I'll start by saying; much of what is said about acetone is based on a misunderstanding of this relatively safe substance. Acetone occurs naturally in our bodies in low concentrations. Much of what's said about acetone is based on fear and misinformation. If acetone smelled like essential oils, few would be concerned about it. Acetone's strange odor and odd feel on the skin make many wary. When properly used, it's a very safe solvent.

Water and acetone are very similar in many ways. They are soluble in each other, which show they are similar. Why? The rule in nature is… "Like dissolves like". Major chemical differences exist between oil and water, which is why they don't mix. Acetone and water also have similar effects on the nail plate, but there are differences as well. Both can absorb into the nail plate however acetone evaporates many times faster than water; that's why it escapes much more quickly from the nail plate than water can, and why it doesn't accumulate in the nail plate, it's always evaporating away. Water wants to stay inside the plate. After acetone is absorbed into the plate, once inside, acetone mixes with the water to form a compatible mixture. These two are so highly compatible, that when acetone evaporates from the nail plate, it carries with it some water from the upper surface layers of the nail plate. The same thing happens when rubbing alcohol and water are mixed; they form a compatible mixture and some water evaporates with the alcohol. Since acetone removes water mostly from the surface, this makes the surface of the nail plate much drier, but only temporarily. Rubbing alcohol or isopropyl alcohol or ethyl ether are examples of other solvents that may be safely used to temporarily remove water from the nail plate's surface. Ethyl ether has also been used for many years as a nail plate surface dehydrator.

When used as directed these nail surface dehydrators will not damage the nail plate. That's because the nail plate is only temporarily dehydrated and dehydration is easily reversed without any damage to the surface. Water flows through the nail plate relatively quickly, these surface cells will only remain in this "drier condition" for somewhere in the range of thirty to forty minutes, depending on the person, or it could take several hours for the plate to completely rehydrate to normal levels. One major and important difference between water and acetone is how each affects the "oil soluble" substances within the nail plate. Oils and waxes come from the nail bed and surrounding tissues and make up typically 5% of the nail plate or less.

Acetone can dissolve and remove these substances from the surface of the nail plate. This adds to the dry appearance created by the loss of water from the surface. These oils can be replaced by using a high quality, penetrating nail oil. Even so, the loss of water has a much greater effect on the nail plate. Acetone will remove more water than oil from the surface of the nail. When this occurs, we say the nail is dehydrated, but only the nail plate's surface is temporarily dehydrated. That is a very important difference. Dehydrating the entire nail is very different from removing only surface water and oil. The latter is what acetone does and does well. We can literally see the effects of dehydration. Removing the water from the nail's surface changes the surface appearance. Light won't easily transmit through the surface to illuminate the nail bed, nor will light reflect nicely off the surface to create what we refer to as "shine". Instead the drier surface is uneven and lacks shine. This is because light is scattered in every direction from surfaces that aren't smooth. This light scattering makes the nail plate appear whitish in places. Now this is really important to understand.

If a drop of water is placed on a dehydrated surface of a nail plate, the lost surface water is quickly replaced. The result is the "white" surface disappears as the surface layers are quickly re-hydrated, since this is the opposite of dehydrating it makes sense that it would happen. Water absorbs into the nail plate at relatively high rates, so as I said before, the nail will not stay dehydrated for very long. Even breathing on the nail plate will start rehydrating the surface. If the white areas don't disappear even after soaking the nails in water, how can the appearance be due to dehydration? Of course it can't be and therefore it is not correct to say the nail is "dry". Yet, this is said quite frequently and it creates confusion.

Often time nail professionals incorrectly blame visible nail "damage" on being "dry nails". This just shifts the responsibility for the problem in the wrong direction. Surface "damage" such as pits and scratches on the nail plate also scatter light in the same manner as surface dehydration. In other words, surface "damage" can also look much like "dehydration" to the untrained eye, but it is not the same. Water is the perfect test for dehydration. If water is applied onto the whitened areas and it doesn't disappear, what does this say? It must not be dry. It's common to mistake surface roughness, pitting or other damage on the nail surface for so-called "dryness". This surface whiteness is caused by scraping the nail plate and forcing residual pieces of nail coatings from the nail plate. This damage is completely avoidable, as discussed in later questions. Try soaking nail clippings in acetone for days, weeks or months. The nail plates will NOT become pitted nor will they develop surface white spots. When you remove the clipping, the surface may look completely white, but a drop of water will reverse that appearance pretty quickly.

22:1 How can I tell if my acetone is pure? The label says its 100% acetone, but what if it's not pure? Can using impure acetone cause lifting if I use it to clean the nail?

Well, just because the label says 100% acetone, doesn't mean that it really is. Likely they are "rounding up" to make a claim of 100%. Salon grade acetone is generally between 97-99% acetone. The rest is mostly water and low amounts of other harmless impurities. Unless of course, you buy a lower grade of acetone. Lower grades of acetone that are bought in paint or building supply stores are less expensive. These are designed for different uses which don't require them to be free from low concentrations of oily contaminants. It is expensive to remove all the oily contaminants, which is why these grades of acetone cost less. Almost all the water and contaminants can be removed to make acetone with a very high purity, but that will cost you ten times more than what salon grade acetone will cost. Purities that are higher than 99% are called "technical grade" acetone. These are typically around 99.5% acetone. Purities up to 99.9% can be purchased, but are extremely costly and this level of purity is not needed for salon applications. Now I want to make it clear that the oily contaminants found in lower grades of acetone are not a safety concern, they just don't work well for salon applications.

Acetone can greatly improve adhesion of any type of nail coating to the natural nail plate. Any grade of acetone is safe for salon applications, when properly used, but the cheaper grades can cause nail coatings to lift or lose adhesion. When the acetone evaporates, these oily residues are left behind and can contaminate the surface of the nail plate with a thin oily film that will block adhesion to the natural nail. This can cause any type of natural nail coatings, including nail polish, UV gel manicures and enhancements to more easily separate from the nail plate. Acetone used to clean the nail plate should not contain significant amounts of these oily substances. Low amounts of water and tiny traces of other non-oily contaminates won't affect adhesion to the nail plate. That's why acetone doesn't have to be 100% pure to be effective for salon use. However, sometimes skin conditioning agents are intentionally added to acetone to help prevent temporary drying of the skin. These additives are useful for that purpose, but may leave adhesion blocking residues on the plate that can increase lifting or cause nail polish to peel more easily.

Acetone with skin moisturizing agents is not designed for cleaning and preparing the nail plate's surface before nail coating application. Here's a good way to test the acetone used in a salon to ensure that adhesion blocking contaminants aren't left on the nail plate. Fill a small glass jar with a small amount of acetone, no more than one ounce is needed and cover it loosely to keep out dust and debris. A shot glass filled about three-quarters of the way to the top, is what I've used in the past, would be about a one ounce or about twenty-eight milliliters. Cover it loosely so that the acetone will slowly evaporate away. Make sure NOT to set the container near any open flames, heat or other sources of ignition where it may cause a fire. Acetone is highly flammable, so place the container in a safe location and where it won't be disturbed or spilled. It could take a week or two for the contents to evaporate completely, depending on the salon temperature. In colder salons, evaporation takes longer.

Once the acetone evaporates, check the inside of the glass container by wiping it with your bare finger to see if any oily residues have been deposited on the walls. If you feel an oily residue, you can be sure these residues will be left behind on the nail plate after cleaning it. Acetone used to clean the nail plate should not contain any amount of oily residues, since its function is to leave the nail plate clean and dry. Good quality, salon grade acetone generally contains at least 1% water. Even up to 5% water is really not an issue, since this low amount will evaporate away from the nail plate as the acetone dries the surface. When properly used, acetone will not leave an oily residue, but instead will remove surface nail oils and leave the nail plate's surface drier for up to thirty minutes. Acetone cannot dehydrate the entire nail, since all moisture cannot be removed from the nail plate, as I've discussed in other answers. Moisture removal is only temporary and mostly occurs within the upper 5% of the nail plate's thickness. That's why I say it dehydrates the "surface". After about thirty minutes, the nail surface will begin to "re-hydrate" itself and will slowly return to normal levels of moisture.

You can see why I say that just because the label says "pure" or "100%" doesn't mean the acetone isn't contaminated with significant amounts of adhesion blocking substances. It might be a good idea to check your acetone if you are experiencing problems with adhesion of nail coatings on clients. When in doubt, it is best to consult with the manufacturer of the nail product of your choice. They may recommend you use a special cleansing agent to remove natural nail oils and improve adhesion.

25:3 We're having a big debate. Is it alright to use "craft" glitters to mix with nail products, instead of those sold specifically for nail use? If not, what's the harm? Aren't they the same thing?

In my opinion, glitters sold for arts and crafts should not be used for nail art application and should never be mixed with nail products. I recommend using only glitters and other colorants that are cosmetic-grade. Not just any cosmetic-grade colorant, you should only use those that are specifically sold for use in nail coating cosmetics. Why? There are several good reasons for why I believe this to be true. Many countries, including the US, Canada, Australia and those of the European Union and others have specific regulations concerning which types of colorants can be used in cosmetics. This is done to ensure safety. Those used for crafts or other non-cosmetic uses are not designed for the type of contact that can occur with cosmetics and may cause adverse skin reactions.

An example of what can happen when improper colorants are used. This was reported in a highly respected medical journal in 2012. Several physicians reported a case-study involving a patient that had come to them with an allergic reaction after wearing UV gel nail coatings for about a year. This 37-year-old housewife had never before experienced any type of allergic skin reaction. For three months, she received artificial nail services from a nail professional and then decided that she could "do it herself". That was the first mistake she made. After about seven months, she developed multiple, intensely itchy sores on the skin surrounding her nail plates and on the palms of both hands.

To determine why she was experiencing this adverse skin reaction, her doctor did a standard skin patch test, this testing exposed her skin to small amounts of a wide range of common allergy producing substances, as well as the nail product she was using. The test results were surprising. The skin testing showed she was NOT reacting to the nail coating product at all, as the doctors may have first suspected. Instead she was having a surprisingly strong allergic reaction to another common allergy producing substance included in the patch testing. She reacted strongly to a substance called "cobalt chloride", which seemed rather odd, until the patient was questioned further. The doctor learned she had purchased some "craft glitters" from the Internet and had been mixing up her own color blends which she applied to her own nails. That was her second mistake. Upon further investigation, it was learned that "cobalt" was listed as an ingredient in the glitters. The cobalt ingredient in the craft glitters was entirely responsible for her allergic skin reaction. Once she stopped using the glitters, these skin problems disappeared.

Cosmetic colorants don't contain cobalt, nickel, chromium, or other such metals, because these are known to cause allergic skin reactions. Not all metals cause skin allergies. Titanium is an example of one that does not. These allergy causing metals and their derivatives should never be used in any cosmetic products. Even inhaling the dusts of these allergy causing metal colorants can be unsafe. It also is important to understand that not all cosmetic colorants are useful for nail application. Some contain special additives that can contribute to nail coating service breakdown. For example, some cosmetic colorants have a silicone surface-coated which can block adhesion and contribute to lifting problems. While others contain additives that allow them to be dispersed in water, making them incompatible with nail coating products. Using these can weaken the nail coating and make them more likely to crack or break.

Responsible manufacturers select and test glitters and color pigments before selling them; they choose those that are safe for use and those which are compatible with nail coating products. This takes out the guess work and helps protect the safety of nail professionals and their clients. Now you can see why I recommend that nail professionals only use glitters and colorants specifically designed for nail products. But there's more, I recommend purchasing only from the manufacturer or their authorized dealers. The Internet is filled with counterfeit products that can be unsafe and may contain potentially hazardous substances that should NOT be used in cosmetic products.

I wrote an Education Update that warns salon professionals about this issue. In that Update I recommend avoiding purchasing any professional salon products from the Internet unless the product is sold by an "authorized" distributor. Counterfeits are often sold by unauthorized dealers, so beware! These can be found all over the Internet. I also recommend sticking to respected, brand name products. Otherwise, you never know what you're getting or what's being used in your services. They may seem cheaper, but they are cheaper for a reason. Most of the time, the safe ingredients have been substituted for cheaper ingredients that may be unsafe. I'll include a version of this Education Update in the Special Topics section, so that you can read it, See Special Topic 19.

28:3 I've heard that when calcium is micronized it can absorb better and that is good for the nails, which is why it is added to some nail products. This sounds fishy, is this true?

I've talked about nail calcium claims before, but not about micronized calcium. I've also talked to marketers who make these types of claims and asked them why. They say that calcium makes strong bones and healthy teeth so it must be good for nails. What? That's their fact-based evidence to support their claims? I don't think that qualifies as "evidence", but instead it's more like wishful thinking. There is no evidence that calcium is needed for nail plate growth, health or strength.

Very small amounts of calcium are found when nail pates are tested; but calcium is only found on the surface of the nail, so likely it comes from the water we wash our hands with. Calcium can dissolve in water and is a naturally occurring component of tap water, as well. This demonstrates that even single molecules of calcium dissolved in water can't penetrate the upper layers of the nail plate. A single molecule is pretty small, so if they don't penetrate, how could a so-called micronized particle that contains a thousand or more molecules? Micronized calcium is solid particles of calcium that have been ground to a very fine powder. The finest talcum powder is micronized, too. Very tiny dusts that float in the air are micronized as well. "Micronized" simply means the powder could be as small as one micron, which is 1 thousandth of a millimeter. So, the claim that micronized calcium absorbs makes no sense.

We could just wash our hands, and that would be better than using micronized calcium. However, because calcium adds no demonstrated benefits to the nail plate, this is certainly a case where size really doesn't matter. My advice is to never be impressed by any nail products just because they claim to contain calcium, of any type.

30:2 What about the removal of these nail coating products with acetone? Does acetone penetrate into the skin and are there any studies that show it is harmful?

"Into" the skin and "through" the skin are two very different things. Acetone does not penetrate "through" the skin or nail plate in any significant amount. Small amounts can enter "into" the upper layers of the skin or nails. Since acetone evaporates so quickly, the warmth of the hand causes very rapid evaporation which drives the acetone quickly from the skin and nails. Before it exits, the acetone will bind with some of the water in the upper layers of skin or nails to cause the water to vaporize along with the acetone, thus drying the surface.

This is how acetone will "temporarily" dehydrate "surface layers" of the skin and nails. It doesn't dehydrate all layers of the skin and nails. That would be impossible. This is just a temporary surface effect. If the skin or nails are wetted with water, they will reabsorb water to rehydrate these surface layers. Rehydration is the opposite of dehydration; both can happen quickly on the surface of the nail plate. Except for the solvent "water", acetone is one of the safest solvents that can be used in nail salons. There are no fact-based studies that I'm aware of that demonstrate acetone isn't safe for nail salon uses. It has been used in salons for many years and has a very long history of safe use. This is why it continues to be one of the most important solvents used in salons, because it is both safe and effective.

Acetone is highly flammable and must be kept away from sources of heat, sparks or flames. No one should smoke when using acetone, nor should it be used near candles, incense burners, etc. Acetone should NOT be heated using a microwave, stove, oven, electrical heater, etc. It can be gently warmed by placing a small amount into a loosely capped plastic bottle which is then submerged into warm water. The water should be no warmer than a Jacuzzi or about 40°C (104°F). Making acetone warmer will also make it more flammable, because it will evaporate more quickly and produce much more vapor. Acetone vapors are what can catch fire and burn, not the liquid. Be cautious when using this solvent to avoid a buildup of high amounts of acetone vapors. Acetone, like many professional nail products should be used in a well-ventilated location.

34:1 A nail professional in Canada asks "why are there toxic substances in cosmetics and why don't manufacturers just take them out"?

This is a very interesting question. One reason this is an interesting question is because this is a great example of what's called a "loaded question". What is a loaded question? It's a question which contains unjustified or inaccurate assumptions. This question contains several unjustified and inaccurate assumptions, can you spot them? The unjustified assumptions are:

1. That there are toxic substances in cosmetics, presumably at harmful levels.

2. That manufacturers could remove these toxic substances, but they don't.

I suspect this person didn't intend to ask a loaded question. She's likely just repeating a question that she heard raised by fear-based advocacy groups who specialize in tricking the public. Using loaded questions is a favorite trick of these types of groups and they are often used to deceive the public. Loaded questions may seem simple, but they rarely have an easy answer. This is done on purpose so the person who is answering will look foolish or like they are hiding something or they are supposedly in denial of the so-called "facts". Let's start with the facts. What are they? Cosmetic products are safe. Not only that, they are among the safest products that consumers can buy. I've heard both **Health Canada** and the **US FDA** make this statement, and I agree with them.

Why is it an unjustified assumption to say that cosmetics contain harmful amounts of toxic substances? This assumes that if a toxic substance is present, it must be dangerous. That is not true and this is a huge deception. Salt is potentially toxic; it can kill. When small amounts are consumed, salt is beneficial and necessary for life. So, the notion that a potentially toxic substance must always be dangerous is clearly an unjustified assumption. This is very important to understand. Most of the claims made by anti-cosmetic groups are based on this incorrect assumption. I'll use the four most widely named so-called toxic substances found in cosmetics to demonstrate what I mean. These four substances are routinely used to trick the public into thinking cosmetics are dangerous. They are formaldehyde, 1,4-dioxane, parabens and lead.

Tiny trace amounts of each of these can be found in some cosmetics, usually at levels below ten parts-per-million which are equal to one-thousandth of a percent. Many of the false claims made by anti-cosmetic groups are based on these exceedingly low amounts that are not harmful. I've pointed this information out to these groups, but their response is always the same. They incorrectly claim there is no safe level for these substances and all the so-called "toxins" should be removed. Why then are apples, apricots, carrots, potatoes, watermelon, mushrooms, plums, cucumbers, spinach and grapes considered safe? These all contain about the same amounts of formaldehyde. Shiitake mushrooms can contain many times more than most cosmetics would ever contain, which is still a very small amount, forty-thousandths of a percent (0.004%). Yes, this is true even when these are organically grown, formaldehyde will still be present naturally because formaldehyde is natural and organic. It exists normally in our breath and blood. Our bodies use formaldehyde as building blocks to make other substances such as proteins. I do agree that formaldehyde exposures should be kept below levels recommended by the highly-respected organization, the AGCIH. They say that exposures below 0.3 ppm (in air) are safe for long term exposures. No nail product would ever produce anywhere near these levels, and that includes nail hardener that contain formaldehyde.

Why are low levels found in plants and cosmetics? Both cosmetics and plants rely on these trace levels of formaldehyde to act as preservatives. Preservatives make these cosmetic products safer, not more hazardous.

What about 1,4-dioxane? These groups like to scare people with this substance because they know many will confuse it with "dioxin" or Agent Orange, which is NEVER found in cosmetics. Dioxin and dioxane may have similar sounding names, but are completely different substances. The names are close enough to scare people and close enough works when the goal is to create irrational fear. These groups know that the average person doesn't know much about chemical names, so that makes it easy to deceive people. Here are the facts; 1,4-dioxane can be found in some nail, skin, hair and body cleansers in tiny trace levels. Why is this so? Trace levels are created as by-products when making certain types of cleansing ingredients. This happens when manufacturer's use a process called "ethoxylation".

It is a myth that manufacturers do this to make cheaper ingredients. That is just another misleading deception spread by these anti-cosmetic groups. This process makes the cleansing agent costlier. Naysayers use this trick to make it appear as if the manufacturers are trying to get away with something. These cleansing agents are much more gentle and less irritating or damaging to skin. Ethoxylation makes mild cleansers for sensitive skin or for use in baby products which must have a low potential for irritation. Some advocacy groups twist the facts and claim there are toxic substances in baby shampoos, washes, etc. which is silly, especially when the facts are fairly considered. 1,4-dioxane is also a naturally occurring organic substance, which these groups will never mention. I wonder why?

Many plants create 1,4-dioxane. They do this to control the ripening of their fruits. That's why this substance is found in bananas, pineapple and tomatoes. I've tested USDA organically grown pineapples and tomatoes that I purchased from a large and well known chain of health food stores. I found 1,4-dioxanes in both. Of course, it would be surprising if I did NOT find these foods since they are known to occur naturally. There are safe levels of these substances, and we should not be concerned about traces.

What about parabens? Fear-based activist groups needlessly frighten people claiming that "parabens" cause breast cancer. This claim was based on surprisingly weak evidence! Just one poorly performed and very small scientific study started this whole controversy. That study has been completely discredited by other researchers performing follow up studies. It has now been determined that these original claims were bogus nonsense. It is wrong to say that commonly used parabens in cosmetics are harmful. These are among the safest preservatives for cosmetics. It is a down-right shame that deceivers have tricked the public into thinking they are harmful. Parabens increase the safety of cosmetics by controlling the growth of bacteria and fungi. They are better at doing this than other cosmetic preservatives. Parabens are also much less likely to cause skin sensitivity when compared to other preservatives.

It is important to note that no country on Earth has banned the use of parabens in cosmetics. Why? They are considered safe as used in cosmetics. This shows the dangerous power that some advocacy groups have widely spread misinformation and intentionally mislead people.

However, there are also other organizations that focus on fact-based information. One example is the well-known breast cancer non-profit organization, the Susan G. Komen Foundation.

Recently they stated that parabens "Do not appear to build up in the tissue from cosmetic use and they have not been found to cause cancer in animals and parabens are not considered a health risk at this time".

Parabens also occur naturally in blueberries, strawberries, black currants, peaches, carrots, onions, cocoa beans, grapes and many other plant sources, even when organically grown. This makes them natural and organic.

Finally, what about lead? Lead is also a naturally occurring substance found in water, air and soil, usually at levels that are well below where they would cause health concerns. In other words, traces of lead can be found everywhere at levels that are considered safe, so lead would be hard to completely avoid. Lead is only a problem when concentrated into much higher amounts than would ever be found in cosmetics. For many years' advocacy groups have been falsely claiming that cosmetics contain dangerous amounts of lead. Lipstick has been a favorite target for these false claims and every few years this myth gets recirculated. This is a hoax that won't die because these anti-cosmetic groups keep it alive. These groups like to keep the public afraid; that's one of their main goals. Lead can be found at around one-thousandths of a percent or less and the US FDA said there is no reason for concern, since they agree these levels in cosmetics are completely safe. The US Environmental Protection Agency allows up to four hundred times more lead in drinking water than is found in lipstick. Health Canada looked at this same issue and calculated that a person would have to eat five tubes of lipstick each day to exceed safe levels for lead ingestion. Yet these groups continue to claim lead in lipstick is toxic despite that the US FDA and Health Canada completely disagree and have said so publicly.

Why is this? These anti-cosmetic groups don't care what anyone says; their minds are closed on the subject. They think they are right and everyone else is wrong. One reason is because these groups don't use real science; they use JUNK SCIENCE! Junk science is phony science; it's the misuse of science to support things that are untrue. In my view, using science to deceive people is a terrible offense. Science is a way to understand the facts, and it should not be used to fool the public. A famous American Humorist Mark Twain once said, there are three kinds of lies, *"...Lies, damn lies and statistics."*

These fear-based advocacy groups get donations from the public and use that money to sponsor bogus studies so they can pretend to have scientific information supporting them. They use this information to create phony statistics that support their misguided causes. This is nothing more than a game of charades designed to fool the public, news media and politicians... while these groups rake in millions in donations. This is why for many years I've asked people to not listen to fear-based activist groups and never donate money to them and don't use their websites. They'll just use the money to unfairly attack cosmetics and continue to needlessly frighten the public with junk science and more trickery. It's not fair and it harms the entire cosmetic and beauty industry. Tell your clients to not listen to these fear-mongers and never donate money to them. They are up to no good!

For instance, last year several well-known health and environmental groups launched a campaign across Canada insisting that manufacturers phase out "potentially toxic" products. Even vitamins, water, and salt are potentially toxic in high enough concentrations. Most plant extracts contain potentially toxic substances, but in low concentrations. Tea tree, lavender oil and many other natural extracts could NOT be used if these groups got their way.

Some may think "potentially" toxic is the same thing as "toxic", but it is NOT. This is how these groups fool the public. In each case above, the concentrations were so low that the presence of these substances was not a concern. I like to quote a well–known Canadian scientist, Dr. Joe Schwarcz who says this about the toxicity of substances in cosmetics, *"Toxicity depends on its concentration in a product and route of exposure, not simply its presence."*

In other words, if the concentration is low enough, there is no toxicity. If a substance is toxic by ingestion only, then it is not harmful to put on the skin. That's what is meant by the route of exposure. For example, it would be safe to rub salt on the skin, even if a doctor instructed the patient to keep salt out of their diet. Dr. Schwarcz is another chemist that is speaking out about the scientific trickery created by these deceptive groups. He's a chemistry professor and the Director of McGill University's Office for Science and Society, in Montreal, where he is also the host of "The Dr. Joe Show" on Montreal's television channel CJAD.

Dr. Joe Show http://www.iheartradio.ca/cjad/shows/the-dr-joe-show-1.1761500

Storage/Disposal

1:2 Do nail products have a shelf life? If so, how can I tell if my products have expired?

Expect to have at least one year to use your products, in general. This assumes they are properly stored; improper storage can dramatically shorten shelf life. The length of that shelf life also depends on the type of product. Nail glues/adhesives are examples of products with much shorter shelf lives. Artificial nail powders are on the other side of the scale and may be usable for three years. Shelf life is extended when stored in a cool, dry location out of direct sunlight. Use up products quickly, while they're still fresh and at their peak performance.

There is often no easy way to tell by looking if a product has an expired shelf life, unless something has gone obviously wrong. Usually the product performance will suffer or it will change in color, odor, appearance, thickness and/or performance.

Examples are:

- Nail monomer liquid or nail glues solidifying in the container.
- Hand lotions that are separating into two layers or develop an unusual odor.
- Nail polish colors that have shifted/faded or is clumpy and difficult to apply.

If in doubt and you suspect a product is past it's shelf life, you can call the manufacturer and ask, but they will need the lot or batch number from the container.

3:1 How should I properly dispose of any remaining acrylic liquid from the dappen dish?

Small amounts can be combined with an equal amount of acrylic powder and disposed of in the trash. Never mix together larger quantities (i.e., more than one ounce/thirty ml). Blending large amounts can become very hot and could create a fire hazard. If you wipe the dappen dish with a towel, seal in plastic bag and put into trash. Take care to avoid skin contact with the liquid monomer. Repeated contact with any artificial nail coating in an uncured state could lead to irritation/allergy.

18:3 I was wondering if you have any scientific backing of what temperature/how to store nail polish? What about cold? Does it damage them in any way or is it ok to store them in the cold?

I'll use the term "nail polish", but what I'll say applies to the other names used for nail polish, such as varnish, enamel and lacquer. Here's something you need to know. In general, heat makes chemical reactions happen more quickly. For example, after being stored for a long while, even an unopened nail polish can become clumpy and difficult to apply. This is due to slow chemical reactions that take a very long time to occur at room temperature. To reach this clumpy stage usually requires more than a year; maybe two, but eventually all nail polish will exceed its normally expected shelf-life and show signs of aging.

However, when nail polish is stored in very warm conditions, the chemical reactions that cause these changes will happen more quickly. The warmer the condition under which the polish is stored, the quicker it will change and lower the shelf-life. Room temperature storage is fine for salons, but keep nail polish out of direct sunlight and away from sources of heat. Also, once opened, the shelf-life will diminish more quickly; especially if the caps are not properly closed to form a tight seal to prevent the evaporation of solvents from the container.

It's best to store nail polish in cool dark locations to extend the shelf life. Some store their nail polish in a refrigerator to keep them cool and extend the shelf-life. This probably isn't necessary and can create problems if not done carefully. Whenever storing products in a refrigerator make sure to bring them back to room temperature "before" opening. If you open the container while the product is still cold, moisture can condense from the air to create droplets of water inside the container that could negatively affect nail polish.

Unusual Conditions

3: Myth- Are white spots inside the nail plate caused by a zinc or calcium deficiency?

White spots inside the nail plate are caused by minor injury to the nail matrix under the eponychium or by immature cells that have never fully developed. Once the injury is repaired, cells revert to normal. Large groups of these under-developed nail cells create a soft spot- take care when filing. You can find more information and a magnified image of these white spots in in the Special Topics section.

17:3 I have a client who suffers from Hyperhidrosis. Her UV manicure is chipping after a week or less. Her nails don't appear "wet" when I apply the base coat and I use acetone to remove her previous coating and a nail prep product. Is there anymore I can be doing? Why does this happen?

Hyperhidrosis is a medical condition that causes sufferers to drip with sweat, excessively. It affects about 3% of the world's population and occurs all around the world. There are solutions, so if you or a client has this condition, seek medical advice on how best to address the issue. Hyperhidrosis can develop even in children and can be a significant challenge to those who suffer with this debilitating condition.

I've known people with this condition and my heart goes out to anyone with hyperhidrosis. Sweat is how we cool ourselves and for some, their cooling system can become overactive. Those with this condition often report difficulty wearing any type of nail coating. I'm not a medical doctor, I'm a scientist and I've looked at the nails of about a dozen people with this medical condition, which is called palmar hyperhidrosis. I found they all had something in common, highly flexible nail plates. That's not unexpected or surprising. I'd be more surprised if they didn't. Why? This type of hyperhidrosis results in higher levels of water in the nail plate. Typically, a nail plate's water content is usually around 15%, but I'd expect it could reach 20-25% in cases of palmar hyperhidrosis.

Normally, water moves through the nail plate at high rates and much of it escapes by evaporating from the nail plate surface. Nail coatings don't stop the movement of water through the plate, but they do slow it down, which causes the water content inside the nail plate to increase, see Image 2 and 3. Nail coatings don't stop water from escaping, they cause more build-up of water inside the nail plate and pack the water molecules between the layers. Think about it, this means that "extra pressure" is also created by this build-up of water. Inside the nail plate the water pressure builds up, which increases the nail plate's "internal water pressure." What's the internal water pressure? That's easy to explain and important to understand. The pressure pushes the water molecules through the nail plate. Imagine a hose that's barely trickling water. If you put your finger on the hose, pressure would eventually build up and cause water to escape wherever it can to leak out, for instance, where the skin and hose make the weakest part of the seal. That's where the water will escape as the pressure keeps building. This is what's happening to your hyperhidrosis client's nails to cause lifting and chipping. Water is moving through her nail plate in extra-large amounts. This causes extra-large water pressure to build up underneath the nail coating.

This pressure would feel weak, but it's there. When the pressure becomes greater than the adhesion of the nail to the nail coating, guess what happens, the coating is pushed from the surface of the nail plate in places where it is the weakest. In other words, the nail plate's internal water pressure pushes the coating from the nail plate. I can't diagnose conditions or prescribe any type of treatment and neither should you, but I want to end by sharing the experiences of some of those I've talked to about their condition.

I've been told by some sufferers that using antiperspirants on their hands helped the condition of their skin and slowed sweating, but didn't help their nails hold onto polish any better, so I assume it didn't prevent the excess flow of water from the bed into the nail plate. I've had others tell me that a treatment called iontophoresis did help with both sweaty hands and improved nail coating adhesion. I assume this is because the iontophoresis also lowered the amount of water flow into the nail plate, thereby reducing the nail's own internal water pressure.

20:1 I have a client that was recently diagnosed with an MRSA infection. I know these are more serious than typical infections, so I wonder if I should refuse to provide her services. Or, should I be doing something different to protect myself? What if I accidentally cut her, what should I do?

For those that don't know, MRSA stands for "Methicillin-Resistant Staphylococcus Aureus". That's a mouthful, which is why this organism is typically called MRSA. This is a bacterial organism that causes infections which are transmitted by direct contact with a surface that has been previously contaminated by a person carrying these infectious bacteria. The infection usually starts in the deeper layers of skin and is not just a surface infection. Typically, MRSA infections form abscesses and may drain fluid. MRSA is a mutation of another more common bacterium known for causing staph infection. The difference is that these mutated bacteria are resistant to many of the common antibiotics that would typically be used to treat a staph infection.

This makes MRSA infections more difficult to treat, but they can be treated and cured. These infections are on the decline, largely because hospitals are doing a better job of preventing transmission of this infection. In general, healthy people with no cuts, abrasions or breaks in the skin have a low risk of infection. Experts estimate that about 1% of the population carries these bacteria, but have no outward symptoms, which makes them "carriers" of the pathogen.

Should you refuse service to a client with this type of infection? No, an infected client is not going to spread an infection simply by touching things. However, if a client has open sores near the area where the service is to be performed, then no services should be provided. That's true for any type of infection. However, if your client has no open or exposed sores that you may contact, the chances of you being infected are extremely unlikely. If you don't cut the client, you probably have nothing to worry about. If you do cut them, then using the proper procedures for cleaning and disinfection when dealing with a cut will ensure you are protected. If you don't know or follow the proper protocols for dealing with cuts, then that's a bigger problem that should be corrected. You can look up "Standard Precautions" on the internet for more information.

22:2 Do you know of any nail polish without wheat in it? My client has Celiac disease and is extremely sensitive towards it.

I don't know of any nail polish that contains wheat. However, I do understand why you would ask. Those with Celiac disease are affected by the ingestion of wheat and/or gluten. When these substances are "ingested" by sensitive people, damage to the lining of the stomach or intestine can cause pain, bloating and a wide range of other unpleasant symptoms. Gluten is not only found in wheat, but also some other grains. Can it cause problems if it were found in nail polish?

No, that is highly unlikely to happen. Even if gluten were found in nail polish, which to my knowledge it is not, the only way it could affect a person with Celiac disease is if they ate significant amounts of the nail polish and no one does that. Even placing your polished nails in your mouth would not be a problem once the nail polish dried. Even so, I don't recommend any one eat nail polish, with or without wheat. I can assure you that it is virtually impossible for any amount of gluten to absorb through the outer surface of the nail plate. That's not going to happen and so there is no need to worry about these substances penetrating the nail plate. The nail plate would completely block any absorption of substances that could aggravate this medical disorder. Gluten is a protein which means it is a gigantic molecule and much too large to pass through the nail plate, same with the other wheat proteins. Gluten is at least eight hundred times too large to penetrate the nail plate. In fact, there is no evidence that these substances can penetrate through the surrounding skin either. In short, I don't know of any fact-based evidence that demonstrates wearing or using nail polish has any harmful effects on those who have Celiac disease.

30:3 A nail pro in the UK asks, "My client has been on hormone replacement therapy for about a month and is noticing her nails are becoming very brittle. Could it be from the HRT"?

Menopause causes many changes in a woman's body. For instance, women lose about 25% of their body collagen during menopause. The result is thinner skin with less elasticity or brittle nails or loss of hair and loss of the collagen from skin. How can a loss of collagen cause brittle nails? Isn't the nail plate is made of keratin, not collagen. Yes, that's true. Keratin is found in epidermis, nails, hair, horns, feathers and hooves.

Collagen is found in dermis, cartilage, bone, and tendons. The nail matrix also contains collagen. Collagen supports the structure of the nail matrix, so a loss of collagen can affect the way the nail plate grows. The matrix is the birth place of the nail plate. Changes in the nail matrix can result in changes to the nail plate. Usually, these changes take one to two months before they're noticed, since that's how long it will take for the nail plate to grow from the matrix and emerge from under the proximal nail fold. Hormones can cause the nail matrix to work more slowly which can make the nail plate grow thinner. Nail plates that grow thinner are weaker and overly flexible. The nail plate can also become more brittle. Those going through menopause most often reported brittle nails; however, people often confuse weak nails for brittle nails. How can you tell the difference?

Weak nails tend to be overly flexible and can crack more easily, especially at the side walls where the nail grows past the nail bed. Also, weak nails tend to split more easily. Brittle nails are not flexible and snap off across the width of the plate, rather than to split down the length. They can also chip or shatter more easily. Some women blame hormone replacement therapy for these problems, but their nail problems are more likely caused by the hormonal changes during menopause. I say this because even women that don't use hormone replacement therapy often report these same types of nail problems. Some women taking hormone replacement therapy report improvements in their nails. What can be done for these types of nail problems? If the nail plate is thin and too flexible, a nail strengthening treatment can help, but these should only be used until the nail plates become more ridged and are no longer overly flexible.

Once the plate reaches the desired rigidity, discontinue use until the nail plate grows out and once again becomes overly flexible. Some nail hardeners containing methylene glycol, aka formaldehyde, and these can reduce the flexibility of the nail plate and will increase nail brittleness, so NEVER use these on brittle nails, only on weak or thin nails with too much flexibility. Daily treatment with a high quality, penetrating nail oil can also increase the flexibility of brittle nails. Weekly hot oil manicures can do wonders for brittle nail plates. Also, newer UV cured treatments which absorb into the upper layers of the nail plate and harden with UV exposure are an effective treatment for thin, weak or brittle nails. These will reinforce and protect the nail plate without increasing nail brittleness.

31:1 I would like to know your thoughts on a new medication that treats fungus on toenails called Jublia topical solution 10%. How does this compare to other medications and what else is effective for fungal nail infections?

Fungi is the name of a large class of microscopic organisms which include yeasts and molds. This means that both yeast and molds are a type of fungi or fungus. Onychomycosis is the medical name for common and long lasting fungal infections of the natural nails. There are more than 1.5 million types of fungi, but only about three hundred types cause human illness and less than five of these causes most nail infections. It is estimated that up to 50% of all nail infections are caused by these five types of fungi. These infections can affect toenails or fingernails but they are much more frequently found on toenails. Largely because wearing shoes provides the ideal environment for their growth- warm, moist and dark- that's perfect for fungus!

As we age our risks for fungal infections increase, most likely because of decreased blood circulation and slower nail growth. Also, various medical conditions increase the risk of fungal nail infections, including diabetes, blood circulation problems and certain medications. Why? These all lower the effectiveness of the immune system, making the body less capable of fighting off invading microorganisms. Contrary to popular belief, nail infections are not caused by our diets and what we eat has no ability to cause nail infections. However, minor injuries that damage the nail or surrounding areas can increase the risks of infections and this probably accounts for most nail infections. This is because fungi are "opportunistic" microorganisms. This means that they won't cause infections under normal circumstances. For instance, they don't normally infect healthy intact skin, but when injury occurs, any break in the skin barrier can allow fungal organisms to infect the underlying tissue. Only a medical laboratory test can confirm a doctor's diagnosis of onychomycosis. Currently the most often used treatments include oral and topical antifungal medications and laser treatments. I'll discuss all three.

The most common treatments for onychomycosis include topical anti-fungal ingredients in creams, lotions, sprays or are incorporated into a nail polish type formula. These topically applied anti-fungal products are the least effective and have the highest relapse rate. This is partially because users need to reapply them for six to twelve months, many give up long before they see any relief and because of poor absorption, which I'll explain in more detail later.

The second most common are oral antifungals. Some are concerned because the oral antifungal medications have been associated with adverse side effects such as a risk of liver damage, even though this rarely occurs. I'm not a medical doctor and can't tell you if you should or shouldn't use any prescription medication. I can tell you what the US Food and Drug Administration (FDA) says about these medications. Both Jublia and Kerydine are two new, recently approved medications for topical use. Both are intended to be applied to the top of the nail and surrounding skin once per day for 48 weeks. These new medications are designed to compete with Penlac, which is also a topically applied prescription treatment that has been on the market since 1999. The most common side effects for both medications are local skin peeling or irritation, e.g. redness, blisters, itching, swelling and ingrown toenails (likely due to inflammation) and some reports of pain or sensitivity at the application site. This is expected to happen to fewer than three out of one-hundred users or 3%.

The studies submitted to the US FDA for Jublia showed that a complete cure happens only for about eighteen out of one hundred users or 18%, so it doesn't appear to be highly effective. However, with Kerydine, a complete cure is expected only for up to 9% of users, that's half as many cured. So Jublia seems to be the more effective of the two. Kerydine doesn't appear to work any better that the older and more widely used topical prescription medication, Penlac. Penlac is applied like a nail polish and is also used up to 48 weeks. It has about the same efficacy as Kerydine, providing a complete cure about 9% of the time, or nine out of one-hundred users. So, Jublia appears to work for twice as many people as does Kerydine or Penlac. But even so, eighty-two out of one-hundred people using this medication will not be fully cured of their fungal nail infection, and will likely relapse. When using any of these medications, the patient is advised to avoid pedicures, manicures, nail polish or having any type of nail service, but that's generally true for anyone with a fungal infection. There are two reasons why the topical nail medications don't work any better than this:

1. The nail plate is a very effective barrier and highly resistant to penetration, making it difficult for topical medications to get past the upper layers of the nail plate.

2. Often these infections occur in the nail matrix and grow out with the nail plate.

Topical medications treat the nail plate only and are not effective against nail matrix infections. Even if the microorganisms in the nail plate are killed, infected nail cells may continue to grow from the matrix area. And if the infection appears to be in the lunula area, more than likely the nail matrix is also infected, making a full cure unlikely with any topically applied medication.

Lamisil is an oral medication which enters the blood stream and is delivered directly to the nail matrix area by the many capillaries that feed and clean the matrix. Because of this, Lamisil is effective for 38% of users, meaning it works for thirty-eight out of every one-hundred people that take the medication for at least twelve weeks. This indicates that oral Lamisil tablets are about twice as effective as Jubila and works four times faster. According to the US FDA 3.3% of patients taking Lamisil in clinical trials had abnormal levels of liver enzymes which is a possible warning sign of liver damage. But 1.4% of people taking a placebo had the same result, so probably less than 2% of these elevated enzyme levels were caused by the medication and only in a few rare cases did this lead to serious liver problems after taking Lamisil, which is why this medication is considered relatively safe.

Now I've heard the stories about Vicks Vapor Rub and nail infections and want to address this myth. It is untrue that Vicks Vapor rub is a useful treatment. A study looking at its effectiveness found that only four out of one-hundred people were cured, so this is clearly very ineffective. Vinegar is not likely to be effective for fungal nails, but there have been no studies that I'm aware of to test this notion. The same holds true for essential oils. I've talked to many people who've tried both vinegar and various essential oils and they report that this failed to cure their toenail fungus and experts I've spoken to agree that these are not useful for this purpose. Therefore, I wouldn't put too much faith in vinegar or essential oils as a treatment.

What about laser therapy? How does that work? One potential advantage of lasers is that they have greater nail penetration than topically applied creams or lotions and therefore are more effective treating infections inside the nail plate. Some medical professionals may file and thin down the nail plate before treatment to make the laser more effective. Lasers also can treat infections in the matrix area, which helps prevent re-infection. Another advantage is those laser treatments are provided in a clinical setting and usually only require one or two treatments, which eliminates the need for months of topical application. How do they work?

Lasers work by selectively targeting the fungal microorganisms with specific wavelengths of infra-red energy. This invisible energy heats up and destroys fungal microorganisms. A very tiny area is heated to approximately 140°F (60°C), which kills the active infection without damage to the surrounding tissues. Some say the procedure can be painful, but most report little or no pain, mostly because the laser pulses quickly rather than running continuously. This minimizes heat damage to other tissue. Several different types of laser therapies are offered. Some are more effective than others. Some are completely ineffective, mostly because the laser being used was not designed for treating fungal infections, so make sure you're being treated by a qualified medical professional with a long track record for treating these infections.

How these laser treatments are performed is just as important as which device is used. I've read reports and talked to doctors and podiatrists about these treatments and most agree that laser treatments only work about 50% of the time, but some medical professionals still doubt their effectiveness and insurance companies still consider these procedures to be "investigational" and therefore will not cover them under medical insurance policies. Some doctors recommend patients take oral Lamisil medication in combination with laser treatments. It is claimed that this combination works best and raises the cure rate to seventy out of every one-hundred clients or 70%. In any case, the patient will need to take care to prevent re-infection, or all their efforts could be wasted. Here are some simple steps to take that will help prevent infection or re-infection.

1. Wash hands and feet regularly and keep nails dry.

2. Disinfect the insides of shoes.

3. Fungal infections thrive in warm moist environments so, wear socks designed to wick away moisture, for example, wool, nylon, polyester or polypropylene.

4. Alternate shoes and don't wear them two days in a row, since it takes about 48 hours for shoes to completely dry.

5. Change socks in the middle of the day to keep feet drier.

6. Wear open toe shoes to reduce humidity.

7. Use anti-fungal powders to help keep feet drier.

8. Wear dry, water resistant gloves to protect hands from excessive moisture.

9. Don't go barefoot in public places, such as pools, showers, locker rooms and hotel rooms.

When all else fails, some patients decide to have their toenail removed and the nail matrix medically destroyed to prevent the nail plate from growing back... which in my view is pretty drastic, but very effective. If you or your client has a fungal infection, my best advice is to consult with a qualified and experienced medical professional, stick with and faithfully follow their advice to maximize the treatment program's effectiveness and don't delay treatment. The longer you wait, the more likely the infection will be to worsen or spread.

31:2 I try to refrain from using the word "Fungus" because people associate this with something contagious. I see this condition more often as we age and the appearance is almost always the same, thickening, yellowing and nail plate layering. What research I have done explains this condition to be more like Candida/Yeast infection and this occurs internally. Candida thrives on warm, moist conditions and a person's diet. Is this accurate?

In general, I don't agree. First, I believe "fungus" or "fungi" are the correct words to use and yes these are contagious. Nail professionals and clients should be aware of this and service providers should not treat these conditions or they risk spreading them to other clients. Second, yeast is a type of fungus and is not the proper word to use, unless a medical doctor has determined that a particular fungal infection was caused by yeast or by a specific yeast such as Candida, they only do so based on the results of laboratory testing. No one can tell just by "looking" at the nail. A nail professional would have no way to determine if an infection is caused by yeast, and to tell this to a client would be considered diagnosis of a medical condition, which is improper for nail technicians to do.

All fungal microorganisms prefer warm, dark, moist environment, not just yeasts. Diet has nothing to do with nail infections and they rarely occur from internal infections, unless a person is suffering from an immune system disorder or uncontrolled diabetes which can also increase risks of nail infections. The overwhelming majority of salon nail infections come from the outside world, not from inside the body. The notion that a client has fungus in their body that infects the nails is not likely. This is highly unlikely to lead to a fungal nail infection for most people. Nail infections are not the same as vaginal yeast infections and their causes are very different, even though the same microorganisms may be involved.

Finally, many things cause the nail to yellow, so this alone is not a reason to suspect a fungal nail infection. The nail plate cannot grow thicker, since the thickness of the nail plate is controlled by the length of the nail matrix, as discussed in other questions. Even so, the nail can appear to be thickening and that is a classic sign of fungal nail infections. Why? Fungal organisms eat keratin. As they digest the nail plate, it begins to fall apart. This allows the layers that are normally tightly packed to now separate from each other. When this occurs, the plate "appears" to be thicker, softer and in advanced stages, it begins to crumble into smaller pieces.

32:3 Can bacteria or viruses grow in a waxing pot by double dipping and in paraffin? I heard that a client a got MRSA from double dipping in a wax pot. Can this happen? Let me know what you think.

I spoke in detail about dipping hands in paraffin when answering a question in Volume 1 (page 80) and explained why double dipping in a paraffin bath to perform salon services is a safe practice and bacteria will not grow in a salon wax. There has been one reported case of MRSA transmitted in wax that I am aware of, but this was related to hair removal with wax, not manicure services. Bacteria can't survive in wax. It needs water to live and there is no water in wax. Dipping hands into wax is different than reusing a brush and spatula. Wax hardens around the hand, so any microorganisms would be trapped against the skin and unable to contaminate the wax. The surfaces/handles of the implements themselves can become contaminated and may transmit infectious organisms, so these must be disposed of after a single use or multi-use implements should be cleaned and disinfected, or sterilized.

What's so different about hair removal verses a hand dip? When hair removal is the goal, the skin and hair follicles have a good chance of being slightly damaged and sometimes there are visible traces of blood. If the skin or hair follicles remain damaged, this temporarily increases the potential for infection, so make sure these areas are kept clean and anything contacting the clients skin is cleaned and disinfected or disposed of properly.

35:2 What is the fuzzy white stuff on the surface of the nail plate after I remove nail polish from my client's toenails? It started on one toe and now other toes have these same spots. They file off easily, so I don't think it is surface damage and they don't go away when the nail plate is wet, so I don't think this is surface dehydration.

I agree, this doesn't sound like surface damage or dehydration. Surface dehydration is quickly reversed when water is applied. There is another possibility that should be considered. This could be a type of fungal infection called WSO, which stands for White Superficial Onychomycosis. W for White, but these can be greyish color as well. S for Superficial, meaning it grows on the surface of the plate. O for Onychomycosis, this is the medical term for any type of fungal nail infection. About 10% of all fungal infections of the nails are infected with WSO.

WSO is an infection of the surface of the nail plate that can be caused by one of a group of three or four different types of fungal organisms. Typically, these organisms infect the upper surface of the nail plate, and have the appearance of white patches or islands. The plate can look like it is covered with white speckled or powdery-looking patches, spots or streaks that appear on the surface of the nail plate. WSO can take on a more powdery appearance as the infection worsens. If they go untreated, these organisms can infect deeper layers of the nail plate.

As the condition advances the nail plate will become rough and crumble easily. The surface of the nail plate may take on a brownish or grayish surface. Since children's nails are thinner, they can infect the entire thickness of the nail plate. The fuzzy appearance that creates the whitish layer can sometimes be easily filed away, but this file can now transmit the infection to other nails. These infections are most often seen on feet, rather than hands since like other fungal organisms they prefer to grow in warm moist environments. They are sometimes seen growing under nail polish and are frequently mistaken for dehydration which results in them being categorized as so-called "nail granulations". But this makes no sense. Nail polish doesn't dehydrate the nail plate; in fact, it does the opposite. Granulations is a term that medical professional use to describe skin that has improperly healed from a bumpy surface and I don't believe it should be used to describe nail plates.

Wearing nail polish increases the moisture content of the nail plate from about 15% water to 20% or more water content, as previous discussed. That 5% increase in water content of the nail plate makes it easier for these organisms to grow. Because these infections are usually restricted to the surface of the nail plate, they can be easier for medical professionals to treat. However, if ignored these organisms can infect deeper layers of the plate which can make these infections more difficult to get rid of, so if you suspect your client has a WSO infection, send them to a medical professional for a proper diagnosis, and treatment if required.

35:3 What is a Koebner reaction? My client had one and her doctor said it was from my manicure, but I don't see how it could be since I sterilize my implements.

The Koebner Phenomena, as it is called, is a skin reaction. It can resemble an infection, but these are not caused by infectious organisms, so even sterile tools can cause these reactions to occur. The Koebner Phenomena occurs when the skin over reacts to injury. A small nick or cut can cause the skin to redden and itch all around the damaged area. Those with psoriasis are the most susceptible to these phenomena. For them almost any type of skin injury is a potential trigger for a psoriasis flare up. The Koebner phenomenon causes new psoriasis plaques to form around the injury. A German dermatologist named Heinrich Koebner first described these types of skin reactions in 1876 when he noticed that psoriasis plaques formed around a dog bite. It is now believed that the Koebner phenomenon affects up to 50% of those with psoriasis and about 10% have a Koebner (KOHB-ner) type reaction every time their skin is injured. Other skin conditions can sometimes be reason for the symptoms, e.g. lichen planus (LY-kin PLAN-us) and vitiligo (vit-ih LIE-go).

Koebner phenomena creates skin damage so the skin becomes more likely to become infected by pathogens. Although the injury didn't cause the infection, the Koebner phenomena makes the skin more susceptible to injury and infection. I was an expert witness once in a law suit where the client claimed to have developed a serious infection due to a manicure, but the nail professional claimed she always properly cleaned and disinfected her implements. Seven days after the manicure the client developed a serious infection on one finger. Based on the evidence and the fact that the client had psoriasis, it was determined that a Koebner phenomenon reaction was responsible for the infection and not the nail professionals cleaning and disinfection procedures.

What else triggers the Koebner Phenomenon?

- Bruises, scrapes, any type of burn including sun, heat, chemical or friction burns, rashes caused by allergies or irritants, tattoos, shaving, manicuring, poorly fitted shoes that irritate the skin, even thumb sucking can trigger a reaction.

- Any part of the skin can be affected by the Koebner phenomenon.

- Nail techs and clients may not associate a nick or scrape with a Koebner reaction since it may take three to twenty days or longer to become visible.

- Researchers have discovered this phenomenon happens more often in winter than in summer and is likely due to exposure to cold weather.

- The longer a person has psoriasis the more like they are to have a Koebner reaction.

- Stress is also known to make psoriasis symptoms become worse and makes the Koebner phenomenon more likely to occur.

How can clients and nail pros avoid the Koebner Phenomenon? One way is to quickly clean and cover any skin wound, which will reduce the risks of an infection developing later. Tell clients to take special care when their psoriasis is active and to avoid scratches, scrapes, or cuts. They should protect their skin by wearing long sleeves and pants, especially when outdoors. If injury does occur, don't pick or scratch since this will increase the chance of developing a psoriasis plaque that has a silvery appearance.

However, if the client develops any signs of skin infection such as redness, pain, swelling, throbbing or warmth at the site of injury, they should see a medical specialist immediately to prevent worsening of the condition. Nail professionals aren't required to know the medical history of their clients, but it would be wise to note which clients have psoriasis and to treat their skin with extra care.

36:1 A nail professional from Germany asks, "Does bleach kill all blood diseases, including Hepatitis C?"

Bleach is a very powerful and highly effective disinfectant that has been widely used since the 1920's. It is the most widely used disinfectant in history. Bleach is inexpensive, easy to use and highly effective, which is why it is often distributed to those who inject illicit drugs like heroin. When properly used, bleach prevents transmission of blood borne pathogens such as HIV and Hepatitis B & C.

When used to disinfect syringes, if they aren't first properly cleaned, it was discovered that if a clot of blood is left in the syringe it may not be properly disinfected. When proper cleaning isn't done, this can result in improper disinfection. In a few cases this has resulted in the accidental transmission of Hepatitis C by intravenous drug users. This isn't the fault of the bleach; this is the fault of improper cleaning. All objects must be properly cleaned before they can be properly disinfected. When this is done properly, bleach is a highly effective disinfectant that is very useful in salons. Typically, it is recommended that the regular, unscented household bleach be diluted in one part bleach to ten parts water. Regular bleach is usually about 5-6% sodium hypochlorite, which is the active ingredient listed on the label. Concentrated bleach is usually 8% of this same active ingredient and should be diluted one part bleach to twelve parts water.

Using more bleach is NOT better, since at too high of a concentration bleach can attack rubber and plastics. The less expensive bleaches labeled as "reduced or low odor" can contain less than 4% sodium hypochlorite. These should not be used as salon disinfectants. However, when properly used, bleach is highly effective disinfectant for salon use. The key, as always, is proper cleaning. It's the most important thing you can do. It's even more important that disinfection or sterilization. Never skip or skimp when it comes to properly cleaning everything coming in contact with the clients' skin or nails.

36:3 What is nail psoriasis and can you tell me what to look out for in my client's nails? Psoriasis of nails mainly occurs in those who already have psoriasis of the skin.

Typically, about 5% of those with psoriasis will have visible symptoms on their nail plates only. Nail psoriasis is seen in about 75% of those with psoriatic arthritis of the fingers and toes. There is no cure for nail psoriasis, and the visible symptoms may come and go and then reappear for no obvious reason.

Nail psoriasis can create dysfunctional nail plates that peel, break or split and may be more susceptible to nail infections. It can also alter the appearance of your toenails and fingernails. They may appear to be thicker and can change shape, color or may feel tender and painful. Nail and skin psoriasis is not caused by pathogens, so it is not infectious and can't be transmitted to other clients. The causes are not well understood, but it is known to have a genetic basis and tends to run in families of all races. Those who have parents or siblings with psoriasis do run about a 20% chance of developing psoriasis as well.

What does nail psoriasis look like? Here are ten things to watch for; any of these by themselves could be related to a dozen different conditions, but when several of these appear together it would be a good idea to recommend that the client show the nail condition to a medical professional, preferably a dermatologist or podiatrist.

1. Underneath the nail plate, the nail bed can develop a discoloration that looks like a drop of blood or oil under the nail plate. These are called "salmon patches", due the pinkish salmon color of the spot.

2. Besides nail bed discolorations, the nail plate may become light green, yellow, or brown.

3. Small pits may develop on the surface of the nail plate as nail cells flake away from the surface. These pits can appear randomly scattered or may appear in straight lines, rows or symmetrical clusters and may have the appearance of small "pin pricks" in the surface.

4. Unusual surface roughness that gives the nail plate the appearance of being filed rough when it has not been filed.

5. Thickening of the nail bed and buildup of a chalky white material under the nail plate.

6. Separation of the nail plate from the nail bed which is known as onycholysis, usually starting at the hyponychium underneath the free edge and extending back toward the eponychium. This type of separation can lead to nail bed infections.

7. Crumbling of the nail plate at the free edge, usually due to the nail plate becoming more brittle. Also, the plate may appear thicker as the layers of nail plate begin to separate.

8. Splinter hemorrhages on the nail bed which appear like tiny black lines running with the direction of nail, growth. Splinter hemorrhages occur when the tiny capillaries in the nail bed break and leak small amounts of blood underneath the plate.

9. Redness of the lunula can also occur if the capillaries in this area become congested or rupture.

10. Nail psoriasis may also create inflammation of the skin around the edges of the nail, which is known as paronychia.

It is safe to cover up nail psoriasis with nail cosmetics, including UV gel manicure or any other type of nail coating. How can you to prevent nail problems related to nail psoriasis? Keep the nail plate trimmed short and file the free edge smooth. Those with this condition should wear gloves to protect the hands while cleaning or doing other work with the hands. They should also use a high-quality skin conditioner to prevent skin from becoming too dry, especially during the winter months.

Wear comfortable, well-fitted shoes with enough room for your toes, especially shoes worn during exercise. Wearing artificial nail coatings can protect the nail plates from becoming more damaged. Be aware of the potential for a Koebner (KOHB-ner) Phenomena skin reaction, since this condition can occur in those with psoriasis. For more information see question 35:3 (above) in this section and make sure to understand this information. Several medical treatments are available, but these are not always effective, depending on the severity of the disease. In severe cases, medical professionals can prescribe medications that can significantly improve this condition, so be sure to refer clients to seek proper medical advice. Because the nail plate takes months to grow, it can take months before any improvement is noticed. Medical professionals often use phototherapy which exposes the skin to UV to treat psoriasis. These treatments expose the skin to many hundreds of times more UV than does a UV nail lamp, so exposing the clients' nails to a UV nail lamp is not likely to produce any healing effects. This is why UV phototherapy treatments must take place in a doctor's office or a clinic. There are about a dozen prescribed medications that may be injected into the affected area, taken orally or topically applied that may help, but only a medical professional can diagnosis any type of psoriasis or provide any therapeutic medical treatment.

40:1 One of my clients has an index finger with bad ridges going from right to left across width of her nail plate. Suddenly she developed a weird green color under the plate. A doctor told her it was infected and he put a hole in the nail to drain it. She lost the nail completely, but it is starting to grow back. Do you have any idea what would cause something like this?

The ridge you are describing is actually a "groove" or depression in the plate. Such grooves are caused when the nail matrix is forced to slow down the production of new nail cells. As long as this slow down continues, the new nail plate growth will continue to be thin. The bottom of this groove develops because the nail plate is making the least amount of nail cells and therefore creating the thinnest nail plate. As the nail cell production increases, the nail plate slowly returns to its normal thickness. Beaus lines is the medical term used to describe this medical condition. They are named after a French physician, Joseph Beau, who first described this condition in 1846. These are indeed medical conditions since they are typically caused by internal health issues. They are most often associated with longer term health issues such as those lasting a month or more. Beau's lines are not caused by shorter term health issues, such as colds or flu. Serious accidents, surgical procedures, long term malnutrition or heavy dieting, serious infections, heart attacks, uncontrolled diabetes or taking chemotherapy drugs can all cause the appearance of Beaus lines.

Beau's lines are a sign that the body is healing. While the healing process is going on, the body diverts energy away from making new nail or hair cells and focuses instead on healing. The appearance of Beau's lines can indicate health issues, when they appear nail technicians should alert the client and recommend they show the condition to a medical doctor or podiatrist. As the medical condition resolves itself, usually the nail plate will return to its normal thickness. The appearance of Beau's lines is also an indication that the nail plate will have a lower ability to resist infection. Bacterial nail infections are sometimes seen when Beaus lines appear, because the nail plate may also lose much of its natural ability to resist infections. Fungal nail infections become more likely as well. In the case of Beau's lines, if there are no visible signs of infection and the nail bed is not exposed, these nails can usually be safely enhanced to camouflage the condition. If the nail bed is exposed, then the plate should not be enhanced for two reasons, the increased risk of nail infection, as well as the increased risk of developing allergic reactions.

One of the most important things to remember is that nail professionals should NEVER attempt to file the nail plate smooth. As I explained, these are not ridges, so if the high points are filed away, the nail technician may cause significant damage to the existing nail plate. Besides over thinning and weakening the plate, this could make a nail infection more likely to occur.

Additional Special Topics

Topic 1 -
Basic Parts of the Nail Update.

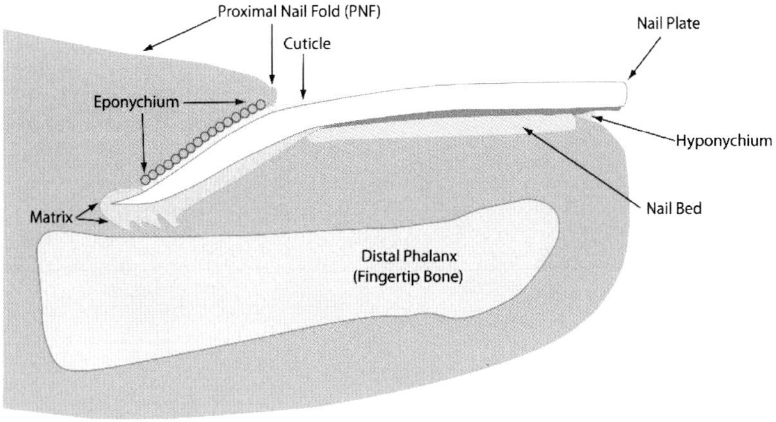

Image 14: Parts of the nail

The following sections on nail anatomy have been updated with the latest information, as explained to me by pathologists and dermatologists who conduct this type of research. As a chemist, I rely on the expertise of those who study the human anatomy. Science and medicine often are based on many competing ideas with the goal of using the best information to determine which ideas are correct and produce the best results.

Nail anatomy is one such area where there are many competing ideas and no real clarity. Not only are nail technicians, manufacturers, trade magazines and the general public confused about the names for the parts of the natural nail, even doctors and scientists aren't sure about nail anatomy and which terms to use. Misinformation is abundant, so it can be very difficult to know the facts.

So, to attempt to clear the confusion, I created a Revision 1 of the nail diagram above and based it on a strict interpretation of the available information. I showed it to many people, including world-class scientists, dermatologists, podiatrists and pathologists. I heard lots of different opinions, as you would expect, but insisted those with opinions had to back it up with hard facts. The information was very insightful and has changed my thinking a bit. The information below should help to clear up long-standing misunderstandings about nail anatomy. Even so, new information often creates new questions that hadn't been considered before, so perhaps there will be more to come... so keep an open mind and I'll always be on the lookout out for the latest nail research.

I believe researchers have uncovered information that answers the question, "*Where does the proximal nail fold end and the eponychium begin?* At last I believe this question has been resolved, at least to my satisfaction.

Proximal nail fold (PNF)- A researcher I worked with made a very insightful comment, he thinks the name "proximal nail fold" is misleading and instead suggested it be thought of as a "flap" of skin that covers the matrix area. Detailed studies of these tissues demonstrate that the PNF the entire flap of skin tissue that covers the nail matrix, and extends only about one-quarter of the way to the first knuckle.

Eponychium- Generally defined in medical literature as the layer of skin which covers the nail matrix and forming nail plate AND is the source of cuticle tissue. Because the thickness of the eponychium was not properly described, this led to confusion. Researchers have now isolated and identified the cuticle forming via highly sophisticated microscopic examinations and have discovered it is a much thinner layer than imagined. These researchers found that the eponychium is only a thin layer, approximate 0.1-0.15 mm thick, and all the cuticle comes from this thin layer. How can such a surprisingly thin area pressing against the growing nail plate be responsible for all this cuticle tissue?

Many suspect the eponychium must be made of a specialized type of cell called an "adult stem cell". These stem cells can create specialized tissue, such as cuticle, nail plates and even hair. Research is underway to verify what many believe and initial studies indicate- the eponychium and nail matrix are composed of adult stem cells that act like factories to produce nail plates and cuticles, 24 hours a day. Unlike hair follicles which have regular growth and resting phases.

Cuticle- is a thin layer of dead tissue derived solely from the eponychium. The cuticle adheres the nail plate to form a seal between the nail plate, preventing pathogens from entering and infecting the matrix area. This should not be confused with the eponychium. The cuticle pulls away from the underside of the eponychium and attaches tenaciously to the nail plate. Nor should the cuticle be confused with the proximal nail fold, since it is living tissue connected to other living skin, while the cuticle is dead tissue directly connect to the nail plate.

Matrix- is where new nail plate cells are created and the nail plate begins to form. New information about the matrix will change the way we view the nail plate, as well. It has been shown that the matrix is not a flattened field of nail cells (adult stem cells) that create the nail plate, as previously thought. Instead, the matrix is shaped like a letter "J" laying on its back with the curved part of the J making up the backside of the nail matrix. This means there is an upper and lower matrix area. The lower matrix is located in a "ventral" position, which indicates it is a "lower" position when compared to the nail plate. (Ventral= Lower/Under) The active nail matrix actually wraps around the backside of the area where the nail plate is formed and hovers in a "dorsal" position to the nail plate, which simply means that it hovers over the top of newly forming plate at the back end, as shown in the image. (Dorsal= Upper/Top).

This indicates that the nail plate on the topside of the nail plate is formed by this dorsal matrix area (upper), while the bulk of the nail is formed by the ventral matrix (lower). This is important information because it sheds light on understanding the structure of the nail plate, but also advances understanding of medical nail conditions such as nail psoriasis.

Nail Plate- is composed of hardened, translucent non-living nail cells that form a solid, protective layer over the underlying soft tissue. This should not be confused with the nail "bed". This is a common mistake made by many, including doctors and scientists, but nail professionals should understand the difference.

Nail Bed- is the soft tissue that sits underneath and supports the nail plate while it slides toward the free edge. This should not be confused with the nail "plate".

Hyponychium- is a soft tissue seal underneath the extended "free" edge of the nail plate whose purpose is to create a seal and prevent pathogens from infecting the nail bed.

Bone- supports and shapes both the nail matrix and nail bed.

Topic 2 - Proximal nail fold damage and pterygium formation.

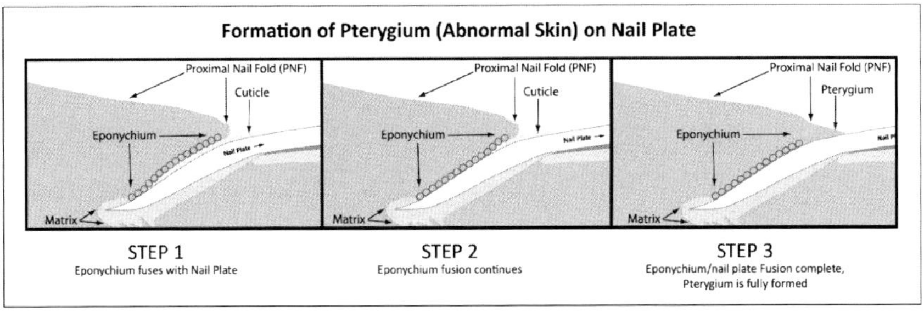

Image 15: Pterygium formation due to eponychium disease or injury.

Cutting any living skin, including the proximal nail fold is unsafe and can lead to infections, which are always possible when the skin barrier is broken or cut. If left alone, this hardened tissue will undergo natural exfoliation, as will the surrounding skin. If all skin cutting discontinues, eventually this area of skin will exfoliate and return to its normal smooth texture and healthy appearance with no cutting required. Clients may insist that the hardened tissue be removed, but it should not be removed by cutting. Instead, supply them with a high-quality nail oil, which will help soften this tissue and improve its appearance until it self-exfoliates- *usually within thirty to forty days*- then the need for cutting will be eliminated!

So-called excessive overgrowth of the proximal nail fold (PNF) can be caused by injury, disease or as a symptom of an adverse skin reaction. Repeatedly contacting the PNF with any type of artificial nail coating materials, including all UV curing gels or monomer liquid and polymer powder formulations, can cause adverse skin reactions to the proximal nail folds and sidewalls.

What many view as an “overgrowth”, may well be a condition called “pterygium” or an abnormal growth of skin that becomes "stretched". Researchers who study these problems believe some types of pterygium occurs because the proximal nail fold fuses with the nail plate, as shown in the Image 15. The fusion is progressive until eventually all of the eponychium is fused to the nail plate. From this point, the proximal nail fold has become fused to the nail plate and will be stretched toward the free edge along with the nail plate in a triangular shape.

The fusion is thought to occur due to injury or disease, e.g. burns, physical trauma, lichen planus, and certain medical conditions also cause this abnormal growth. Such conditions should be referred to a doctor for examination if they have an unhealthy appearance. Pterygium should not be cut away by nail technicians, since it can bleed and become infected. It can be softened and conditioned, e.g. hot oil manicures.

The proximal nail fold is living skin and is **NOT** the cuticle and should never be confused for cuticle tissue, especially by nail professionals specializing in the care of the natural nail. To reduce the potential for confusion, it is important to use the proper terminology when speaking about the parts of the nail. As you can see from the images, cuticle tissue hitches a ride on the nail plate as it grows. This thin layer of cuticle tissue is an important barrier (seal) that helps keep bacteria out of the nail matrix area. An infection in the matrix area could lead to permanently damaged nail plates or if unchecked could spread to infect the bone. Cutting and overly aggressive manicuring or pedicuring of this area can break the tissue seal to allow bacteria to penetrate and cause a nail to become infected, which is why it is important to carefully manicure this area.

Topic 3 -
Nail plate growth and plate penetration

The portion of nail plate on the bottom (green) comes from the lunula, which is the front-end area of the ventral nail matrix. The term "ventral" indicates it is the part of the matrix that's lower or below the nail plate. The upper nail plate (blue) derives from the dorsal matrix. The term "dorsal" indicates that it is the upper matrix, above the nail plate. The center of the plate is produced by the middle matrix area (violet). Not a lot is known about the differences in behavior of these different areas, but this is an area of active research.

The top portion of the nail plate is unique and formed by the dorsal matrix area. The term dorsal means "upper". These nail cells create a dense protective layer that seals the upper nail plate and prevents most substances from penetrating. There are unique features related solely to the upper most layers of the nail plate. For example, this top layer is prone to be affected by a condition called "nail psoriasis", which affects about 75% of those who have skin psoriasis. This condition appears to affect the dorsal nail matrix and causes weak attachments to form between nail cells as the nail plate forms. These weak attachments lead to formation of small surface pits where nail cells have been displaced and are missing- which is a characteristic feature of nail psoriasis.

The center area of the nail (purple) comes from part of the ventral matrix and provides the nail plate with strength and flexibility, while lunula (the front edge of the ventral matrix) produces a thin layer (green) that appears visually different when viewed via scanning electron microscope (SEM). It has been suggested this layer works in conjunction with the upper nail layers to seal and protect the center portions of the plate. This is one of several reasons why the nail plate is very difficult to penetrate. It's a myth that ingredients or any other substance can easily penetrate through the plate. That's not likely to occur with most substances.

Special penetration enhancers (only a few exist) must be used to get medications into the center portion of the plate and even they don't work very well. A normal, intact natural nail plate is notoriously difficult to penetrate by chemical substances. Any substance that absorbs past even the outermost layers won't get far. Instead, these substances concentrate just below the surface, mostly within the upper 10% of the nail plate's thickness and may appear as a discoloration or stain. It is tempting to file away the stain, but this can significantly thin and weaken the plate- by removing 10% or more of its thickness. It is usually better to cover up the discoloration with a protective nail coating or nail color, rather than file that much of the nail plate away.

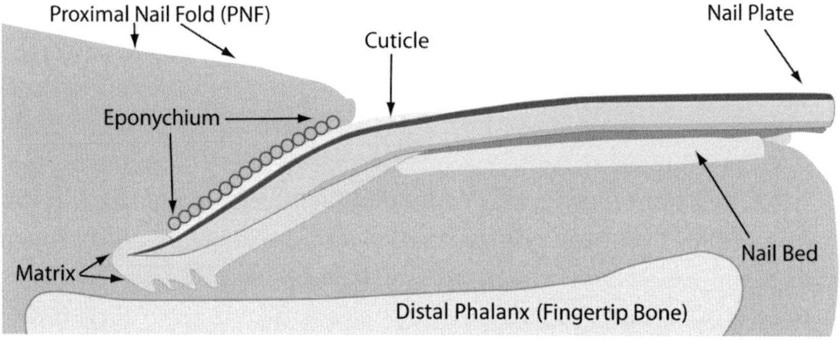

Image 16: This is a cross-section demonstrates the matrix is divided into three parts or zones: bottom, middle and top...
divided into three parts or zones: bottom (green), middle (gray), top (blue).

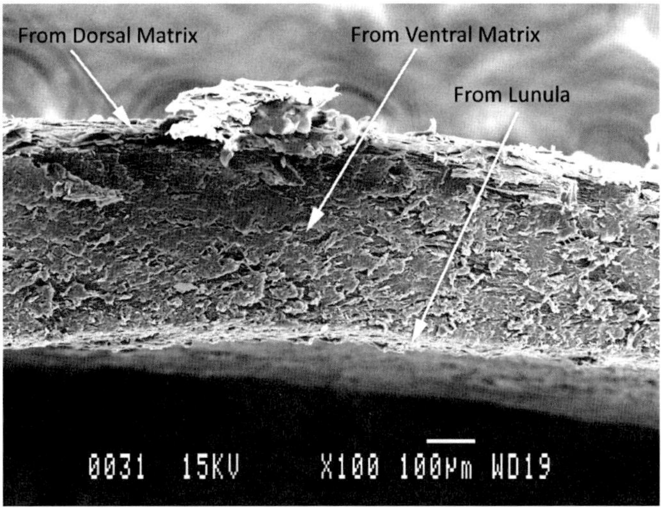

Image 17a: A cross-section of a nail plate after magnifying 100 times to reveal three, visually different layers that comprise the nail plate.

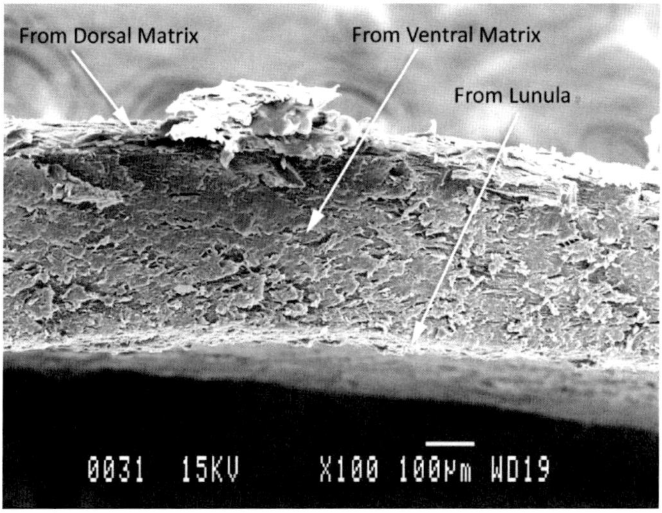

Image 17b: Note the upper and lower layers, highlighted in blue to make them more visible, on the upper and lower faces of the nail plate which are derived from different parts of the nail matrix.

Topic 4 - Nail Plate Surfaces

The topmost layer of nail cells in the plate form a tight, chemically resistant "seal" that isn't affected by pH changes that would alter the shape of hair cells and cause the hair's cuticle to lift away from the shaft. This allows for seepage of substances inside the hair shaft, but this doesn't occur in nails and is one of several reasons why nail plates remain resistant to absorption of external substances.

Certain dyes can stain the nail plate. Early nail color formulations used high concentrations of staining dyes. Now-a-days, better quality, professional nail polishes contain low levels of dye and avoid those that permanently stain the nail plate. In general, nail discoloration is caused by dyes, damage, drugs, disease, injury or illness. Base coats can help prevent staining, so they do much more than just to improve nail polish adhesion. Base coats help seal and protect the plate from staining the natural nails, as well as to help prevent discoloration of artificial nails. Normally, the nail plate is resistant to stains, but damaged plates are more absorbent so colorants absorb deeper into cracks, splits or pits in the plate where they concentrate and become more visible.

Some substances which can penetrate the top surface of the nail plate, can't move easily beyond the upper layers of the nail plate and therefore they become trapped inside the plate. Nicotine stains are a good example. More and more nicotine builds up near the surface making the stain grow darker and more pronounced. Damage to the surface of the nail plate allows some substances to penetrate more easily, but most will be trapped in the upper layers of the nail plate and not able to penetrate beyond into the middle layers. Of course, if the nail plate is cracked completely through to the nail bed, penetration becomes much easier, which explains why the nail plate should be kept thick and intact. Breaks or cracks can allow complete penetration to the nail bed below. Normally, relatively few substances can penetrate through the nail plate in significant amounts. The natural nail is a powerful barrier that's not easy to overcome.

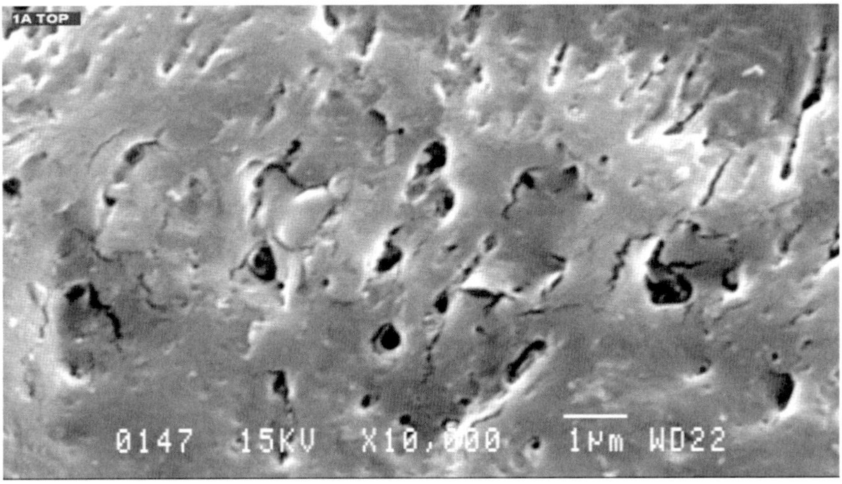

Image 18: Surface of the nail plate magnifed 10,000 times to reveal tiny defects and openings which allow for surfaces to be stained.

Topic 5 - Nail plate over-filing is an avoidable, yet a common problem.

Over filing is one common cause of nail damage. When people say, "artificial nails ruined my natural nails", they're often referring to damage from over filing. A heavy-hand use of a coarse abrasive (e.g. 120 or 180 grit) or an electric file can quickly remove half these layers, leaving the nail plate overly thin and weak. Even a wooden pusher can scrape and damage the nail plate if excessive downward pressure is used. Avoid a heavy hand and the client's nails will thank you.

Don't use below a 180 grit on the natural nail plate, and only with a very light touch. More preferably a 240 grit should be used. In careless hands, a 180-grit hand file (or electric file) may create considerable nail plate thinning/damage, so these should be used cautiously. It is unwise to use coarser files or electric files directly on the natural nail. A good rule to remember: the lower the grit, the easier it will be to create nail damage. That's because lower numbers indicate there are fewer, but bigger abrasive particles on the nail file. Bigger particles make deeper and wider scratches into the nail plate. Over filing can make nails plates overly flexible, which will negatively affect adhesion- for both nail polish, UV gel manicures and artificial enhancements. For many reasons, you should always strive to keep the natural nail plate thick and intact.

In my observations, I've found that many nail professionals over file the natural nail plate, some filing away as much as 50% of the plate's thickness. There is a better way- only remove the "surface shine"- not layers. Carefully/thoroughly clean the nail plate, taking time to use proper nail preparation procedures. If the nail is visibly thinned, e.g. a ledge exists between the filed plate and new growth; then it is safe to say that over filing probably occurred. A nail professional's job is to protect and beatify the nail plate, not file or scrape it away. This is achieved by filing lightly on the very topmost layer. When it comes to filing the natural nail, less is best. Keep those nail plates thick!

The images below show the effect of grit size of the abrasive file when used on the natural nail. The nail plates are all magnified by 400 times to make the surface scratches more visible for comparison. The nail files have each been magnified 2000 times, to make it easier to see how widely the particles vary in size and shape.

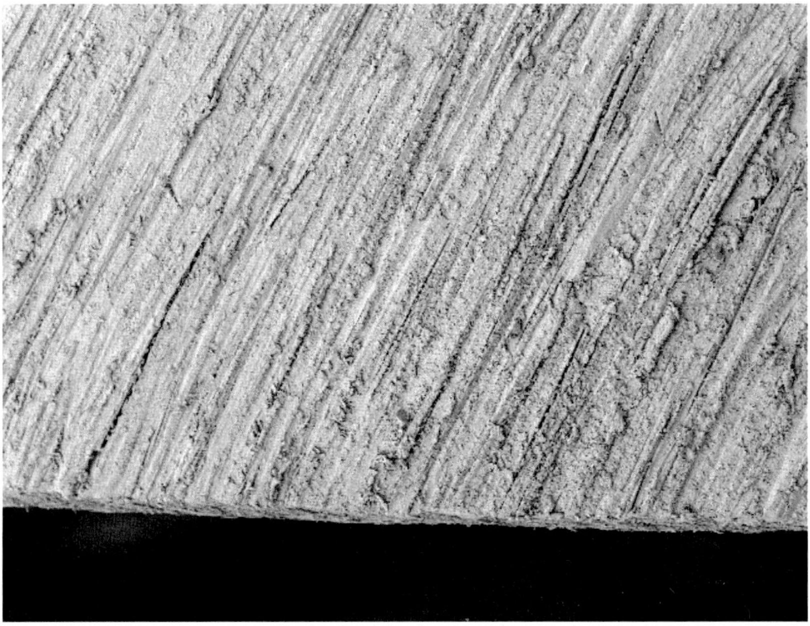

Image 19a: Magnified nail plates filed with 240-grit file

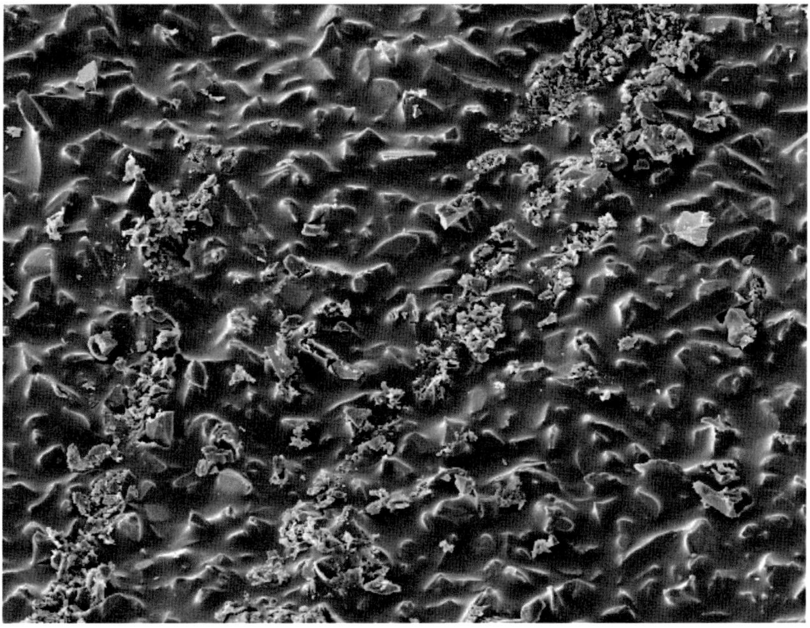

Image 19b: Magnifed surface of a 240-grit file.

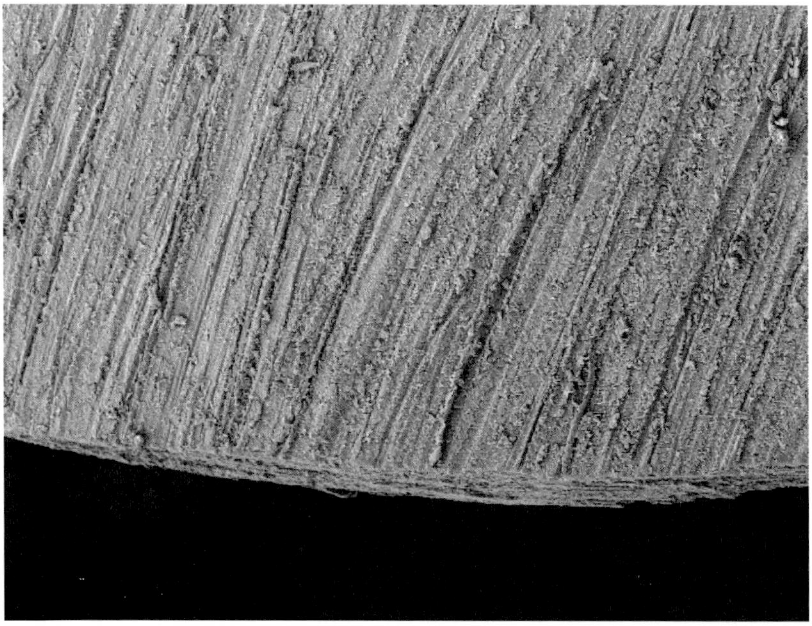

Image 20a: Magnified nail plates filed with 180-grit file

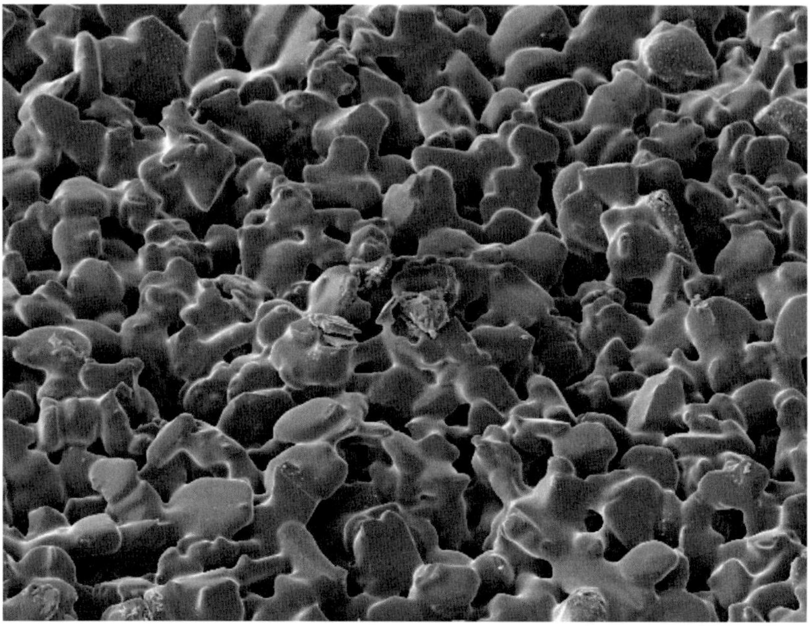

Image 20b: Magnified surface of a 180-grit file.

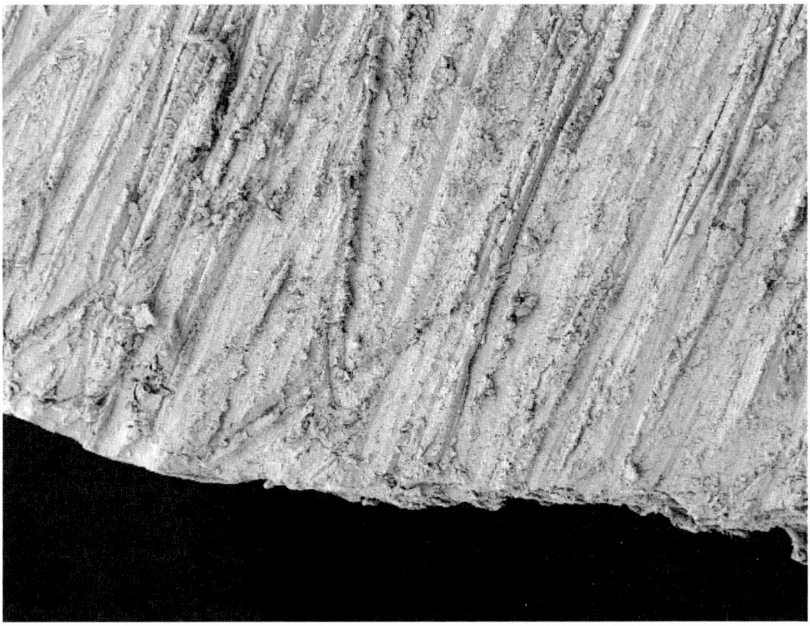

Image 21a: Magnified Nail plates filed with 120-grit file.

Image 21b: Magnifed surface of a 120-grit file

Topic 6 - Normal growth pattern of the nail plate and free edge peeling

Why does the free edge seem to always peel on the top side, rather than the bottom side, as shown in the image below? This is due to the nail cells normal pattern of movement. The following image traces the path taken by nail cells as they are pushed from the matrix to the free edge. Some nail cells travel much further than others, depending on where they were created within the nail matrix. Nail cells on the top of the nail plate originate from the dorsal matrix, which is much further from the free edge than the lunula, which is the leading edge of the nail matrix. Normally (depending on growth rate), it would take approximately 50-60 days for a nail cell to move from the back end of the matrix to the front edge of the lunula. So, the nail cells which traveled this route could be almost two months older than the nail cells directly below that are just being created by the lunula. Therefore, the oldest nail cells on the plate are found at the upper surface of the free edge.

These nail cells have more time to pack together and harden into a sheet. This helps to improve the surface of the nail plate beforehand so it can better endure and resist the environmental effects from constant exposure to the outside world along with all the daily insults and abuses the nail plates are forced to endure for months on end.

The nail cells made in the lunula area of the matrix will have a very different experience. These cells make up the bottom-most layer of the nail plate. These cells are only exposed to the outside world for a relatively short period as they emerge to create the underside of the plate's free edge. Because the underside of the free edge is exposed to much less detergents/handwashing, sunlight exposure, etc., normally the nail plate will rarely peel from the underside of the free edge.

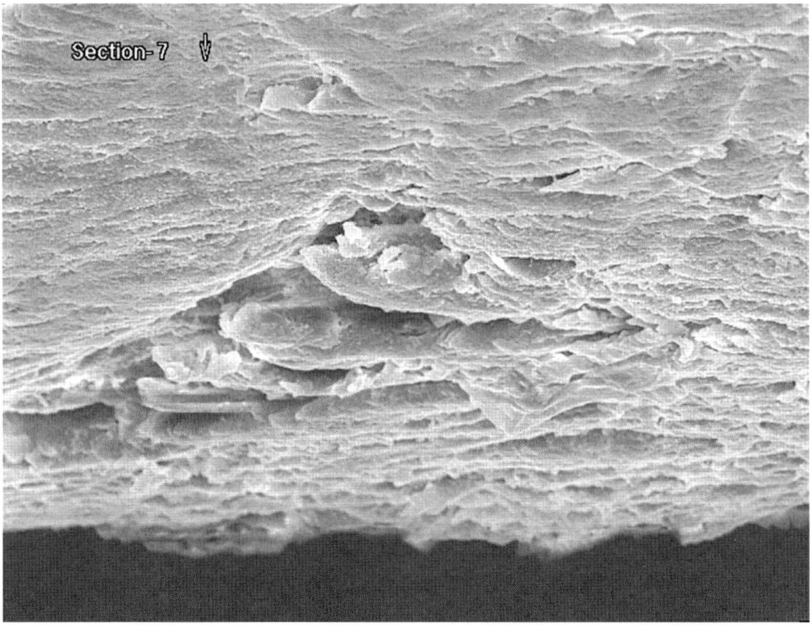

Image 22: Peeling free edge of a natural nail plate, approximately 100 times magnification.

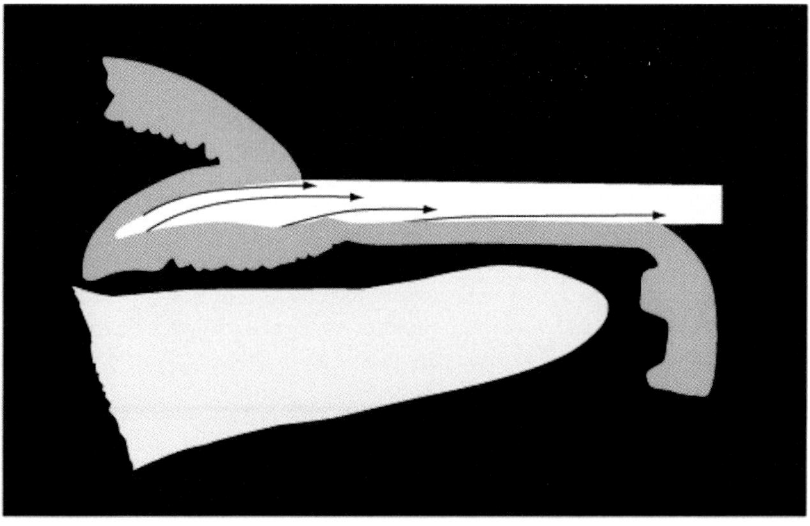

Image 23: Nail cell movement patterns. The oldest nail cells on the plate are found at the upper surface of the free edge.

The eponychium is the living tissue which covers the nail matrix and is the source of cuticle tissue on the nail plate. It is now known that the thickness of the eponychium is much thinner than previously thought. Previously, the eponychium was considered to be all of the skin that covers the nail matrix, but medical researchers have now isolated and used advance techniques to identify the eponychium as a much thinner layer than previously thought, only 0.1-0.15mm thick. It is this thin layer of eponychium cells that lead to the development of the cuticle. The eponychium is a surprisingly thin area pressing against the growing nail plate and attached to the underside of the proximal nail fold.

Proximal nail fold (PNF)- the English language uses the word “fold” to describe this area, but in other languages this translates into nail “flap”, to describe the entire flap of skin that covers the matrix area. This is living skin and should not be cut. Like a callus on the foot, the PNF’s leading edge can “harden” in response to repeated cutting with cuticle nippers or other sharp tools. This should **NOT** be done in a nail salon because it can lead to infections.

Topic 7 - There are NO ridges in the nail plate, only grooves.

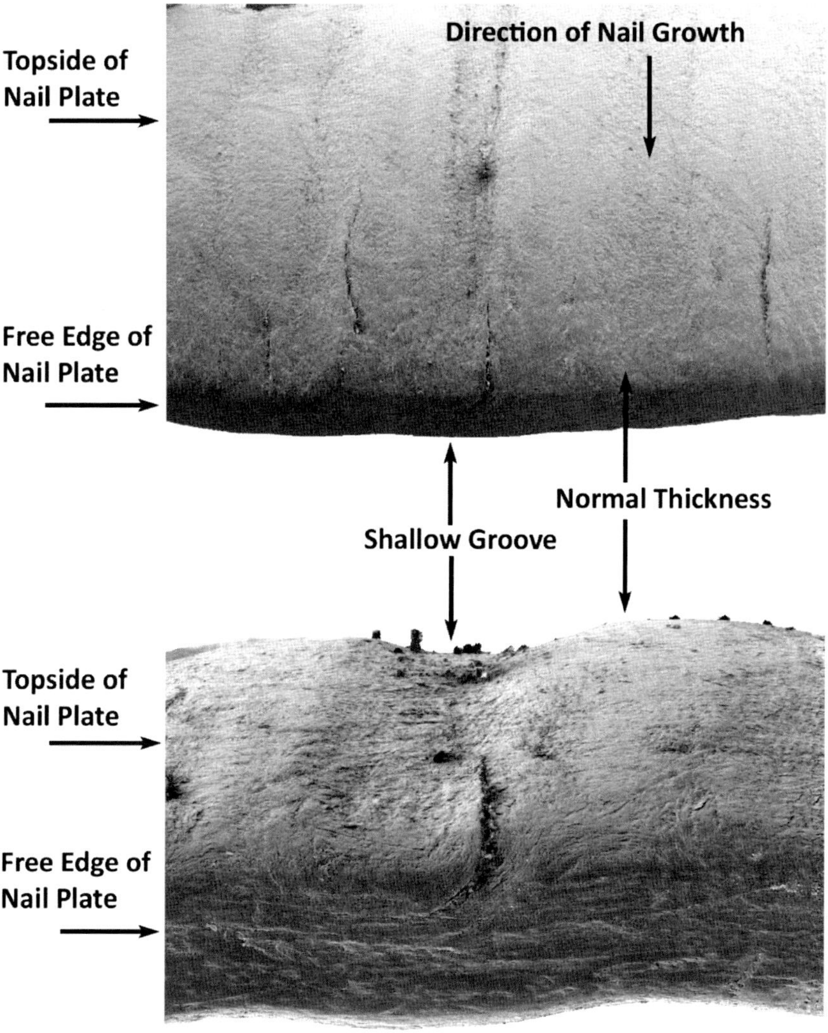

Image 24a: This shows grooves in the nail plate (top and side view).

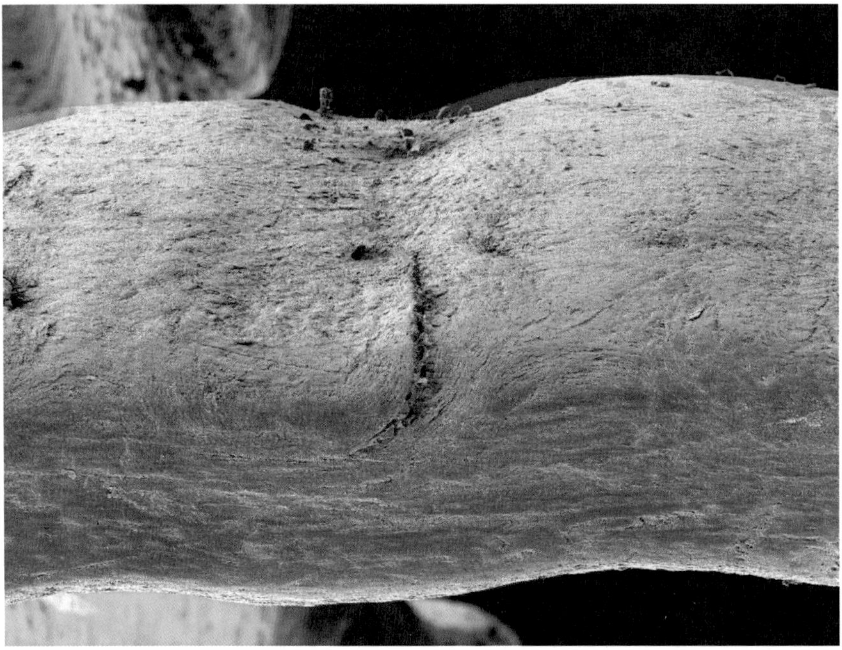

Image 24b: 3D image of a groove running the length of the natural nail. ***Red****/Cyan 3D glasses required.*

The length of the nail matrix determines the thickness of normal, heathy nails. The deeper the matrix, the thicker the nail. It is far too common for nail technicians to buff the nail plate smooth to remove so-called "ridges", but surprisingly, there are no ridges on the nail plate to be removed. The nail plate can't suddenly start growing ridges. That's not possible due to the way the nail matrix produces nail cells. Instead, the nail plate develops shallow grooves where the aging nail matrix works less efficiently making new nail cells. It is very common and quite normal to see grooves on nail plates of people older than 30 and is considered a normal sign of aging.

Problems can occur if the surface of the nail plate is filed to remove these high points. This filing reduces the entire nail plate to as thin as the deepest groove on the plate. Yikes! Any attempt to remove this part of the plate, which represent its normal thickness, will merely thin and weaken the entire nail plate.

Rather than thin the nail plate to match its lowest point, it is far better to keep the client's nail plates thick! Nail coatings, including nail polish, don't adhere well to overly thin nail plates, so the reduction in plate thickness often leads to poor adhesion of any applied nail coating. Excessive plate thinning can also cause the nail's surface to peel excessively and/or crack at the free edge.

When the nail plate develops these grooves, rather than filing the surface smooth, it is far better to use an opaque base coat to fill and cover the grooves. This will maintain the thickness and integrity of the nail plate. Overlaying the nail plate with a thin layer of any type of artificial nail coating can also camouflage the groove and reinforce the nail plate, while improving its appearance without over thinning. In the long run, this is a far superior method for improving the appearance of the client's nail plates. There is no need to make the nail plate thinner, when it's relatively easy and better to cover and hide normal grooves that run the length of the plate.

Topic 8 -
Surface White Spots:
Damage or Dehydration?

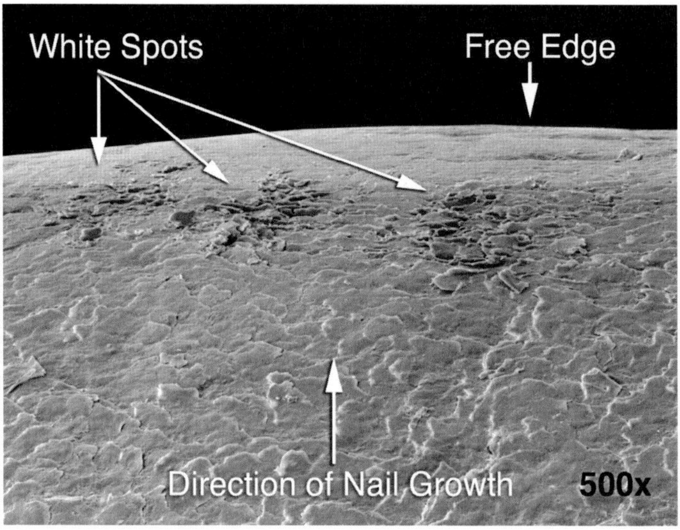

Image 25a: Improper removal of UV manicures can cause surface white spots on the nail plate.

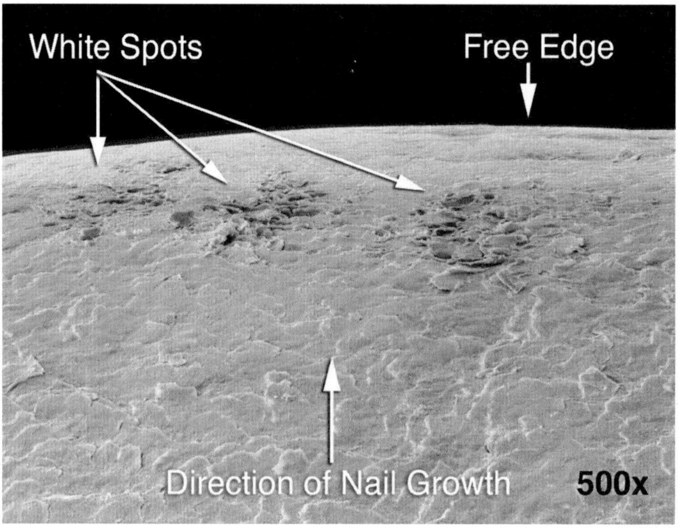

Image 25b: 3D image of surface white spots, Red/Cyan 3D glasses required.

UV gel manicures are safe, useful salon services that require proper application, maintenance and careful removal. Clients should not be allowed to extend wearing time beyond what is recommended, e.g. two weeks. This type of nail coating typically becomes more difficult to remove the longer it remains on the nail, reaching peak removal difficulty after about four weeks. Improper curing by using an incorrect nail lamp can also make UV nail coatings more difficult to remove.

A common myth claims that surface white spots on the plate after removing UV gel manicures happen due to dehydration, but that doesn't make sense. Think about it. If these types of surface white spots remained after washing/soaking hands in water or repeated applications of hydrating nail oils, they probably are not due to so-called "dehydration". The word "hydrate" means to add water; "dehydrate" means to remove water. For instance, soaking in a tub of water will hydrate the nails while soaking in acetone will remove water and "dehydrate" some water from the nail plate's surface, but that will not cause permanent white spots. When nail dehydration occurs, the surface of the entire nail plate contains less water, not just in some spots. Also, any dehydration will be quickly reversed by soaking in water. Another example can be seen with the use of "nail dehydrators". These products are used before applying monomer and powder (L&P) nail enhancements and will leave the entire surface of the nail with a chalky white appearance. However, when you apply water to the surface, the chalky white appearance disappears immediately. That happens because the nail's surface is no longer dehydrated- "dehydration is reversible". Clearly, if a nail dehydrator doesn't cause white spots, it is VERY unlikely that acetone will dehydrate the nail to cause white spots. Try soaking a nail clipping in acetone for a week to prove this to yourself.

Additional images shown below demonstrate the causes for these types of white spots; the surface of the plate is harmed by the damaging forces created by scraping and/or prying. It's easy to see these nail cells have been uplifted and pushed out of position to cause reflected light to scatter, creating a whitish appearance.

Proper removal requires UV gel manicure nail coatings to be soaked in removal solvents, typically acetone or blends of acetone and other solvents or additives. Acetone is most often used because it's fast-acting and has a very long history of safe use for nail related applications. When sufficient time is allowed, these remover solvents will gently break apart the coating. Removers also soften and break the adhesive bonds attaching the coating to the nail's surface. With sufficient time, this can be accomplished without causing any significant natural nail damage, but the use of force should be minimized or completely avoided when removing these coatings.

More force is required when the nail coating has not soaked for a sufficient period, so more soak time should be allowed. Forceful scraping or prying techniques with any type of pusher, wooden or metal, can dislodge many layers of nail cells, creating tiny pits across the natural nail's surface. This is the cause of the three white spots in the image above. The UV gel manicure coating isn't what's damaging the nail plates; this damage was created by improper application and/or removal techniques. To avoid this type of damage, treat the nail plate carefully while performing these types of services. No filing is best or very minimal filing with a 240-grit abrasive, depending of the system used.

Topic 9 -
What to do about unhealthy nail conditions?

A nail professional asked me once what she should do when a new client walks into her salon with an unusual growth of tissue on her nail unlike anything she had ever encountered. She wasn't sure what to do or say, so she asked for my input. Here is my view on such things; only licensed medical doctors can properly diagnosis a medical condition of the hand and by her admission, this clients nail was clearly not normal or healthy. If she attempted to diagnose this condition, it would be a clear violation of the law in most countries. For instance, in the US, federal law expressly forbids anyone, other than a licensed medical doctor or podiatrist from diagnosis of any medical conditions of the nail, and for good reason. This includes any unhealthy nail, finger, hand, or foot conditions. The same likely holds true no matter what country you work in.

When it comes to these types of medical conditions, only medical doctors can "diagnose", "treat" or "prescribe any treatments". If we attempted to replace the doctor and provide our own opinions, we aren't doing the right thing for the client. From any perspective; legal, medical or moral, it is always best to instruct the client to see a physician before providing any nail salon services to unhealthy nails. That's best for everyone concerned, especially the client.

Always refer such issues to a medical doctor for a proper diagnosis and treatment (if required). Don't play doctor and don't let your clients use you to replace their doctor. Doing so could cost you your professional license and you may become a party to a lawsuit, or damage the reputation of your salon, should something go wrong or if the condition worsens.

Topic 10 -
Damage on surface of the nail creates surface white spots on the nail plate.

When small white spots appear on the nail plate after removal of any UV cured nail coatings, a likely reason is improper removal. Fortunately, most this type of nail damage is completely avoidable. How? By taking the appropriate amount of time, care and caution when removing UV nail color coatings, precisely following the manufacturer's instructions, and fully heeding all recommendations. That's good advice for removing any type of UV nail coating.

How can nail damage occur? Soaking the natural nail for even a few minutes in acetone or water will temporarily soften the surface making it temporarily more susceptible to damage from any implements that pry, push or force the remaining residual UV coating from the nail plate. Instead, a good rule to follow is, "*use the utmost care for 60 minutes after immersing natural nails in any liquid for more than 60 seconds.*"

Below are four magnified images using a scanning electron microscope, to show the result of natural nail damage caused by improper removal of UV nail color coatings. These images were also shown in Volume 1, but with a much briefer discussion.

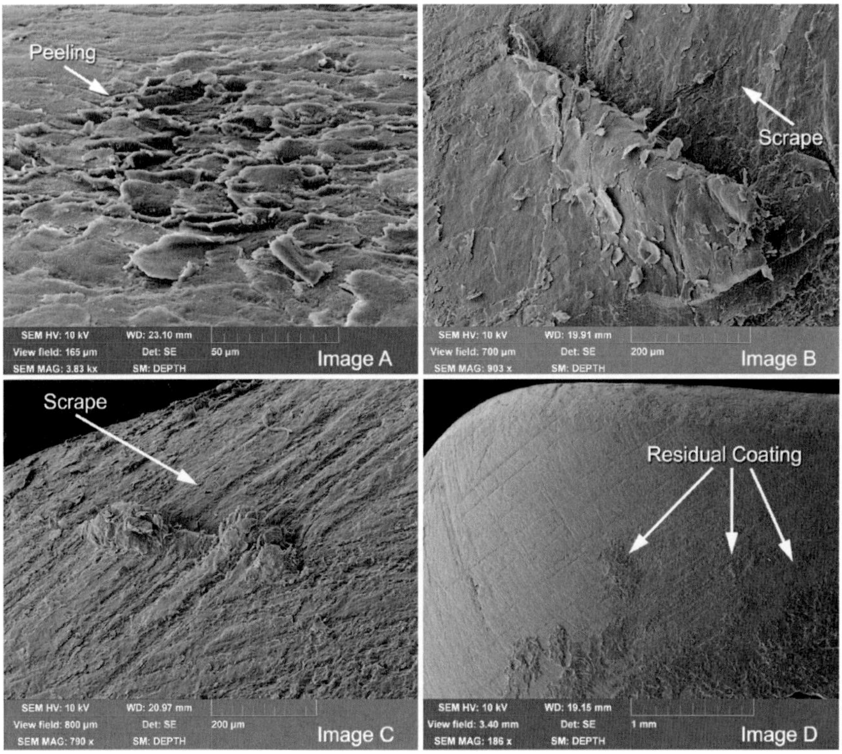

***Image 26a** magnified over 3000 times and shows damage caused by "prying" residual UV coatings from the nail plate. A large cluster of these can create the appearance of white to off-white spots or patches.*

Image 26b and 26c *demonstrates that even a wooden pusher, which was used on these plates, can damage softened nail plates and bunch up nail cells like a throw rug sliding on a slippery floor. Look closely and you'll see where a wooden pusher created the wide gouges leading up to these damaged areas that range in size from one half to twice the thickness of the human hair and smaller. Imagine the damage a metal pusher and heavy hand could do. The spots are small, but many of them bunched together create the appearance of a diffused white spot in the nail plate. Fortunately, this type of damage is avoidable for most people if these coats are properly removed. UV nail color coatings may not always be suited for every nail type, e.g. problematically thin, weak or broken nail plates that expose the underlying nail bed. As always, nail technicians should use their professional judgment when assessing a client's suitability for any nail service.*

Image 26d *is a nail magnified only 186 times, so that more of the nail plate can be seen. This demonstrates that the surface is scattered with islands of UV nail color coatings which were not properly removed. This is often how the damage starts. Overly aggressively scraping with any implement significantly increases the risk of surface damage. Filing away the residual coating with an abrasive can lead to excessive nail plate thinning. It's best to follow manufacturer's instructions and/or always allow sufficient time to properly soften the coating with an appropriate remover before attempting to remove it from the nail plate. If the UV coating hasn't sufficiently softened, continue the soaking process until the coating may be removed without damaging the nail plate. Don't rush! Always take the necessary time needed to completely soften any UV coating before gently removing with a cautious approach and careful touch.*

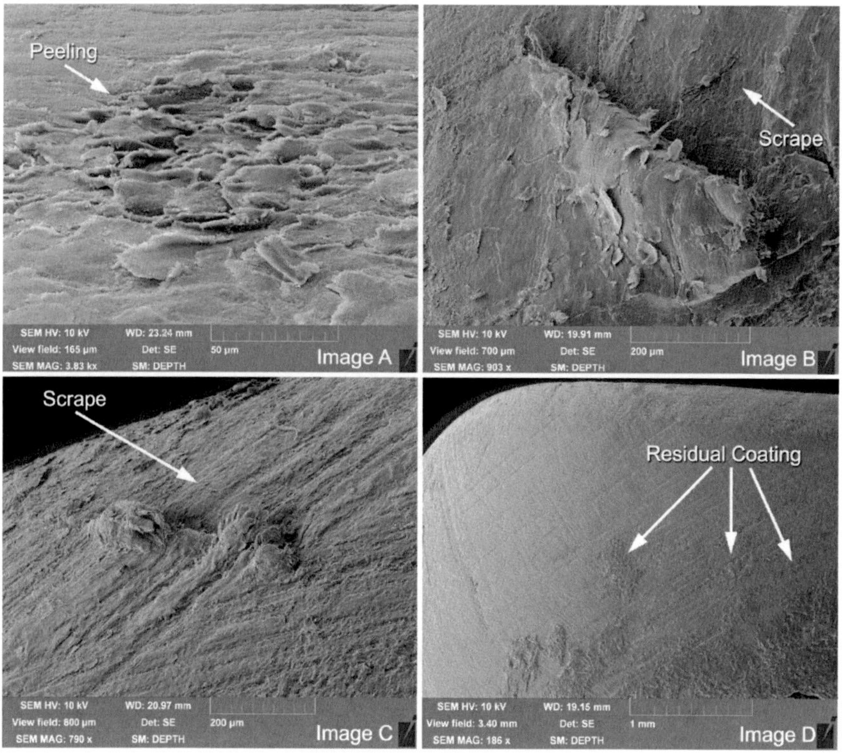

Image 27a-d: 3D version of Image 26a-d (above),
***Red/Cyan** 3D glasses required.*

Topic 11 -
Disinfect or Sterilize?
Which is Better for Salons?

To disinfect or to sterilize? That is the question I'm often asked by nail technicians and the media, however this isn't the right question to ask. Why? It's not about "which", but instead "how" and "when". Salon related infections would be rare if all items used in performing nail salon services were either disposed of or they were properly cleaned and disinfected, e.g. exactly follow the label directions. Even so, the rate of salon related nail infections is comparatively low considering the many millions of salon services safely performed each year. The risks have been exaggerated by some, but a client is unlikely to develop an infection because of a salon service. Infections do occur, but fortunately not often. In general, clients can expect a safe visit to visibly clean nail salons that practice proper cleaning and disinfection OR properly use an autoclave. Both are good solutions for the salon environment.

Regardless of the relatively low rate, this is not an excuse for continuing business as usual; in fact, a big change is needed in the nail technicians' thinking. Unless the thinking of some changes, this will continue to be a big black eye for the industry; costing untold millions in lost salon service money. What a shame. I believe the very best thing that could happen to the salon business is if all nail technicians began routinely practicing proper cleaning and disinfection. If I had three wishes for the nail salon industry, that would be my first one. Wow! Public perception would change, salon business would soar to new heights and appointment books would always be full! I dream of that day and believe it is coming. Nail educators and nail technicians working together can make this happen by working on social media and at the local level, around the world; no country is exempt from this issue.

One way or another, this issue is holding back everyone in this industry. Too many salons take short cuts or use unclean/contaminated implements or files. Some believe the solution is for salons to use autoclaves because they represent a "higher standard". That's not going to solve this problem. Autoclave use can make some client's feel safer, but in practical terms; they don't make a service any safer than when proper cleaning/disinfection procedures are in regular use. When a salon infection occurs, it's more likely because of a failure to properly clean/disinfect; NOT because the salon didn't have an autoclave. Failure to properly perform these procedures is the problem. It makes no sense to suggest that proper cleaning and disinfection isn't effective enough for salons. Only a certain few items can be placed in an autoclave and everything else will still require proper cleaning/disinfection, e.g. pedicure bowls, armrests, doorknobs, cash registers, plastic items, etc.

Properly cleaning and disinfecting should be a main goal for all salons. In addition, autoclaves are useful tools when properly used, regularly tested and kept well-maintained. Salons that don't regularly perform these tasks are probably better off using proper cleaning and disinfection procedures for everything in the salon. Salon disinfection products are proven effective through scientific testing, as required by Health Canada, U.S. EPA and others. Autoclaves and disinfectants both, must adhere to government standards. Use these properly and per the product label or manual; they will help keep your clients safe and protected.

Topic 12 -
LED and Proper Curing

There is a lot of confusion about LED Lamps; can they be used to properly cure any type of UV curing nail product? The answer is no! It is true that all LED lamps create UV and will harden UV curable products, but unless the LED lamp was specifically designed to properly cure this particular UV nail product, don't expect to achieve a proper cure- except by luck. Traditional-style fluorescent and LED-style UV nail lamps both cure UV nail products by emitting low levels of UV energy. It's not surprising that the many available nail lamps have differing ranges of UV wavelengths and widely differing intensities. It is common for two different brands of LED nail lamps to differ in wavelengths and intensity. The same holds true for traditional UV nail lamps; different brands are highly unlikely to have the same UV output. Each of these lamps will cure a UV curing nail product to varying and different degrees.

A properly and carefully formulated UV curing nail product requires the correct level of UV exposure in the proper range of wavelengths at the correct intensity and for the right amount of time. All three of these factors are of equal importance and none of these should be ignored. This is true for every type of UV curing nail product; hard, soft, soak-off, hybrids, etc. UV curing nail products can cure to three levels that are best described as; “under cure”, “over cure “and “proper cure”.

Too little UV exposure results in under curing; too much exposure results in over curing. Under curing can lead to service breakdown and increase the potential for skin sensitivity issues, while over curing can lead to excessive heat that can burn the nail bed to cause onycholysis- which could eventually lead to nail bed infections. Nail professionals that disregard manufacturer’s instructions or don’t use the correct lamps with proper cure times are “curing to the eye”. They don’t realize that hardening is NOT always a proper cure. Nail products will harden when they achieve 50% cure, so a hardened nail coating may not be properly cured. Natural sunlight will also cure UV nail products, but that doesn’t mean that sun-curing is a sensible thing to do. These sophisticated products must be used and cured properly. The best way is to follow the directions of the UV gel manufacturers and don’t let a nail lamp manufacturer instruct you on how to cure a product they don’t manufacture themselves! Nail lamp manufacturers should NOT be instructing nail technicians to disregard UV gel manufacturer’s directions and recommendations. Note: Some UV gel manufacturers have tested several nail lamps and based on their testing, may recommend the use of several lamps. Even so, there is no nail lamp that can properly cure all UV gel products. There are way too many UV gels for this to be practical.

The same types of rules apply when cooking. If you put cookies in an oven that’s too hot, they will over cook. If the oven is too cold, they will under cook and it doesn’t make sense to just leave them in until they “look like they’re probably cooked”. Instead, follow the label created by the manufacturer who has provided the proper cooking time and temperature. Nor does it make sense to completely ignore the instructions and put the cookie dough in the microwave for a half the time, unless you want improperly cooked cookies. What if these cookies are to be sold to a client? Wouldn’t the client rightly expect their cookies to be properly cooked? The same holds true for UV curable nail products! Proper UV product use requires correctly curing with the proper UV lamp, whether traditional or LED.

Topic 13 -
What are the facts about UV nail lamp safety?

I once gave a presentation on UV nail lamps to a large group of scientists and engineers who specialize in using UV to cure all types of products. Everything from Italian lacquer wood, dental and medical prosthetics to DVDs, newspaper ink and flooring; you would be amazed at how many diverse applications exist for UV curing. This group of UV experts was interested in learning about UV nail products and lamps, so they invited me to speak. Also invited was Dr. Robert Sayre, an internationally known scientific expert on the effects of UV on human skin and one of the inventors of the SPF rating system for sunscreen products. Dr. Sayre and his partner Dr. John Dowdy actively research the effects of UV on skin and eyes and has tested many widely-sold brands of UV nail lamps, including LED lamps. They are internationally known and respected PhD level photo biologists who understand how to properly test UV devices and have done so for decades. Dr. Sayre's presentation and mine were in complete agreement that UV nail lamps are safe as used, when used appropriately and in accordance with all manufacturers' instructions. Here are some highlights of those presentations, which are based on their peer-reviewed and published scientific research.

- UV nail lamps are safer than natural sunlight or sunlamps.
- UV nail lamps properly belong in the least risky of all categories.
- UV nail lamps used in salons have a UVA bulb that is vastly different from anything used for indoor tanning.

- Physicians are grossly exaggerating exposures, the safety questions raised about UV nail lamps were successfully addressed by two independently performed laboratory studies of UV lamps.

- The most comprehensive study was performed by two internationally known scientists, Dr. Sayre and Dr. Dowdy.

- Drs. Sayre and Dowdy determined that UV nail lamps are nothing like tanning beds. Both the lamps and UV levels are different. UV nail lamps produce far less UV light with different ranges of wavelengths than tanning beds, so they are NOT equivalent.

- Skin is never burned or tanned, even with regular use of UV nail lamps.

- Services are performed once every two or three weeks, with each hand exposed for a total of 6 to 10 minutes.

- UVB output is far less than natural sunlight exposure.

- Testing by Sayre and Dowdy shows that the proper category for UV nail lamps is: "No hazard with 16.6 minutes of exposure." (per internationally accepted standards).

- Clients can expect there will be no hazard to skin when exposed continuously for 16 minutes. Typically, client exposure is less than 10 minutes and not continuously, over several shorter intervals.

- No risks to the eyes are expected from UV nail lamps under normal conditions of use.

- If clients are still concerned they can wear SPF 15+ broad-spectrum sunscreen or cover the hand with white cloth to eliminate exposure. Note: UV shields for hands are also available on the Internet.

- Sayre, Dowdy and I agree- the scientific evidence demonstrates that all types of UV nail lamps are safe as used, when used appropriately and in accordance with all manufacturers' instructions.

Topic 14 - Safety of UV nail lamps.

I want to review a comprehensive 2013 scientific study concerning the safety of LED-style and traditional Fluorescent-style UV nail lamps (aka UV nail lamps) that is very important for several reasons:

1. This is the first study to compare six major brands of UV nail units, including three that use UV producing LED bulbs as the UV source.

2. It is also the first and ONLY study to adhere to the official internationally accepted standard for UV source testing (ANSI RP-27) which is determined to be the superior method for evaluating UV nail units.

3. This independent study was performed by two world leading UV/Skin researchers Dr. John Dowdy and Dr. Robert Sayre. Dr. Sayre is one of the inventors of the SPF rating system for sun screens and both are considered world-class experts and scientific leaders in the field of research related to UV and skin exposure.

4. The results demonstrate the safety of a wide range of top selling UV nail units (aka nail lamps) and show they are well within accepted safe levels.

My Analysis and Quotations:

- This study is superior to any previously performed testing on UV curing nail units, because it follows the correct scientific protocols and uses the proper testing equipment necessary to comprehensively evaluate the safety of UV nail lamps.

Some other studies by inexperienced dermatologists utilized inexpensive, $150 UV meters purchased from the Internet, but these are incapable of producing valid results. Drs. Sayre/Dowdy used a $50,000 research grade UV spectrophotometer that met the internationally accepted requirements for proper UV device testing.

Very few will read this highly technical paper (see link below), so I've provided my analysis and commentary, along with pertinent quotations from the study. To be clear, **only the *italicized texts* in quotation** are found in the *Dowdy/Sayer paper* and **everything else is my commentary** about the reported results from this important study.

- Not only does their study provide strong evidence that UV nail lamps are safe as used in nail salons, the researchers found the UV nail lamps were even safer than they expected, *"All of the various UV nail lamps submitted for evaluation were found to be significantly less hazardous than might have been anticipated based on the initial concerns raised..."*

- The paper cited important research demonstrating the natural nail plate is a very efficient blocker of UV, protecting the nail bed, "*... the UV exposure risks to the nail bed is comparable to that of skin protected by high SPF topical sunscreen.*" Research studies indicate the nail plate's natural UV resistance is comparable to the UV resistance provided by an SPF 40 sunscreen.

- Also cited was additional research to demonstrate that the backside of the hand is 4 times more resistant to UV than the forehead or cheek. It is 3 1/2 times more resistant than a person's back, making the backside of the hand THE most UV resistant part of the body, "*The dorsum [backside] of the hand is the most UV acclimatized, photo adapted, and UV-resistant body site."*

- The study provided conclusive evidence to demonstrate that UV nail lamps are not like tanning beds, *"When UV nail lamps evaluated in this report are compared together with these earlier sunlamp computations, we find that the UV nail lamps are vastly less hazardous"*.

- Because the measured UV exposure was so low, a person could go to their workplace and once every day put their hand under a UV nail lamp for 25 minutes and this would still be within the "*permissible daily occupational exposure limits*" for workers, per the applicable international standard (ANSI RP-27). Obviously, salon client exposure is much, much lower and just a tiny fraction in comparison, also it must be considered also that client exposure is only twice per month. This scientific paper provides powerful evidence to further support the safety of UV nail lamps; either traditional tube or LED-style.

- This study also demonstrates that risks for development of non-melanoma skin cancer (NMSC) are very low when compared to normal noon sunlight. Of the types of UV that can cause NMSC, this study found that UV nail lamps exposed skin to somewhere between 11-46 times less than NMSC related exposure expected from spending equal time in natural noon sun light, "*...the UV nail lamps had 11-46 times less NMSC effective irradiance than an overhead 1 atmosphere solar spectrum [normal noon sunlight]."*

- These researchers put things into perspective when they concluded that it is very unlikely that anyone could become overexposed to UV through normal use of the nail lamps tested since they considered it, "*...highly improbable that even the most dedicated nail salon client or avid home user would approach this level of exposure."*

- The researchers noted this *"Notwithstanding the comparatively trivial UV risks associated with UV nail lamps there are some reasonable and potentially serious concerns involving these devices that should be discussed."* Special care should be taken in cases where potential users are taking medications that increase UV sensitivity. These individuals have been, *"... advised against venturing into natural sunlight without proper protection and should be cautious about using UV nail lamps."* Of course, that is very sensible advice that should be heeded!

- What was the most significant risk these scientists identified? Concern that the incorrect replacement lamp/bulb may be inserted into the UV nail unit, e.g. those emitting UV-B or UV-C could be harmful to the skin if accidently inserted. Also, the incorrect lamp/bulb can lead to improper curing of the UV gel. For several reasons, it is VERY important that UV lamps/bulbs are replaced with the exact same UV lamp/bulb that was supplied with the UV nail unit when it was purchased. In other words, use ONLY the UV nail unit manufacturer's recommended original equipment (OEM) lamp/bulb replacement.

- When sharing his opinions based on the nail lamp testing Dr. Sayre has said that some, *"Physicians are grossly exaggerating exposures."* And of UV nail lamps he says, *"...this UV source probably belongs in the least risky of all categories."* And, *"UV nail lamps are safer than natural sunlight or sunlamps."*

I wholeheartedly agree with these statements and the results of this study. There are several other studies also demonstrating the safety of UV nail lamps. Now this information needs to get into the hands of physicians so they can make proper recommendations based on science, not misinformation. The same goes for the media news outlets. You can do your part, by sharing this information with everyone you know, including your clients. If you see unfair misinformation being propagated, please share this information. The Dowdy/Sayre study should convince any reasonable person about the safety of UV nail lamps.

Dr. Dowdy and Sayre's full text scientific paper is available from this link to the publisher's website

http://onlinelibrary.wiley.com/doi/10.1111/php.12075/abstract

Dowdy, J. C. and Sayre, R. M. (2013), Photobiological Safety Evaluation of UV Nail Lamps. Photochemistry and Photobiology, 89: 961–967. doi: 10.1111/php.12075

Topic 15 -
Can UV cured nail gels be over cured?

Yes, but over curing is avoidable. Over curing happens in two ways; 1) too much UV energy is used or 2) the nail coating is exposed to significant levels of UV after leaving the salon. In other words, UV nail coatings can be over cured in the short-term and/or long-term.

When a nail coating is exposed to too much UV energy, it will cure too quickly. This can lead to service breakdown, nail damage and even nail infections. How? All UV nail coatings release small amounts of heat when they cure. This explains why some clients feel a slight warming. When over cured, the same UV gel coating may become very hot, resulting in a painful nail bed burning sensation.

For example, a layer of nail coating designed to be properly cured for two minutes under a fluorescent-style UV nail lamp can heat up quickly when cured under a LED-style UV nail lamp, heating the nail bed in excess of 120°F (48°C), which can result in painful burns that may lead to nail plate separation (onycholysis). Onycholysis allows bacteria easy access to the nail bed, making infections easier to occur. Over curing can make nail coatings more difficult to remove, which can lead to nail damage. Why?

Surface white spots often occur when products are scraped from the nail plate with too much force. When nail coatings are more difficult to remove, scraping damage is more likely.

UV gel nail coatings can also be affected by tanning beds and natural sunlight. Poorly formulated or incorrectly manufactured nail coating products are more likely to be brittle, discolor, crack, break or lift (i.e. excessive free edge chipping) and it's often due to continued UV exposure. Certain ingredients used in lower quality nail coatings can turn dark brown or become yellow with continued UV exposure. Long term UV exposure can cause some nail coatings to lose their flexibility and become more brittle.

How can nail technicians avoid over curing nail coatings? One of the best ways is to always use the UV nail lamp specifically designed for the UV nail coating product of your choice. Follow manufacturer's instructions and heed all warnings.

Properly maintaining the UV nail lamp is of great importance. Replaceable UV bulbs must be changed on a regular basis to ensure proper curing. Heavily used UV nail lamps may need bulb replacement every three months; moderate use may require bulb replacement twice per year. It is very important to use the replacement bulbs supplied by the UV gel product/lamp manufacturer. Never substitute for another UV bulb type or brand. Incorrect bulb use results in improper curing and potential hazard to the client's skin as some bulbs are not intended for use with UV nail lamps. High quality UV bulbs may cost more, but in the long run trying to save money by buying less expensive bulbs is likely to cost far more than it saves.

Topic 16 - UV lamps found to be safe by medical researchers at Massachusetts General Hospital and the Alpert Medical School at Brown University

The facts and truth about the safety of UV Nail Lamps is once again confirmed by an independent study from medical researchers at Massachusetts General Hospital and the Alpert Medical School at Brown University. These independent scientific researchers have confirmed the safety of these lamps. This latest report states conclusively, *"UV nail lamps do not appear to significantly increase lifetime risk..."*.

This study noted that medical doctors often use UV medical lamps as a therapeutic skin treatment and when compared to such medical devices which have been in long use, *"...one would need over 250 years of weekly UV Nail sessions to experience the same risk exposure."* They also stated that, *"Dermatologist and primary care physicians may reassure patients regarding the safety of these devices."*

This is now the third group of world renowned researchers to study UV nail lamps and declare them safe and unlikely sources of skin cancer, thus confirming the original statements released after the Nail Manufacturers Council on Safety (NMC) concluded their initial study in 2009. Unfortunately, some misinformed individuals have ignored the growing body of evidence which has all along demonstrated that UV nail lamps are safe as used in salons. These uninformed opinions have created significant problems for nail technicians everywhere by needlessly alarming and even frightening away potential clients.

We can't change the past, but we can join forces and proactively work together to ensure that the facts are made known. Please share this information with everyone you know. If you've seen negative stories on your local news or favorite TV show or read a blog that propagated misinformation, please take the time to forward this educational update to these sources and ask them to correct their past statements. This will undo some of the harm caused by erroneous reporting. Even so, this will likely be a long struggle, so please be vigilant and keep this information handy over the coming months while together we set the record straight and show the world that UV nail lamps are indeed safe!

Topic 17 -
A review of three common myths

Myth 1: Nails Need to Breathe.

No, they don't! There is no reason to believe that nails need to "breathe". Nails aren't alive and don't have lungs nor do they have any ability to absorb air into the nail plate. This myth makes no sense on many levels! In short, nails do NOT require an external air supply and do not breathe or exhale. 100% of the oxygen needed by the nail matrix to create a new nail plate comes from the blood stream and 0% comes from the outside world. Everything the nail plate needs to properly grow and function is delivered and/or removed by the blood flow to the matrix area and nail bed. The matrix is where the nail plate is created from nutrients which can ONLY be delivered by the blood stream. Neither "air" nor "nutrients" can be absorbed or "fed" to the nail plate from any external source.

Moisture and natural nail oils leave the nail bed and pass through the nail plate at slower than normal rates, but they aren't "trapped". The nail plate's moisture content is increased by 10-15%, and the oil content increases only slightly; both serves to increase the flexibility of the natural nail plate. Waste products are removed from the matrix area and surrounding tissues by the blood as well, and are not released into the nail plate. Normal, healthy nail plates would continue to grow and thrive in a completely air-free environment, if a healthy flow of blood to the nail is maintained, so clearly... nails don't need to breathe!

Myth 2: Nail coatings are bad for the nails.

This is NOT correct. Nail coatings don't harm the nail plate and any nail damage is usually a result of improper application and/or removal. If the nail plate underneath the enhancement is much thinner than the area of new nail growth, this strongly indicates excessive filing with a manual or electric file. Overly aggressive filing causes most nail plate damage seen in salons. This isn't done just in discount salons, it happens even in high end salons and is indicative of an improperly trained nail professional. If upon removal the plates are not any thinner, but feel like they are overly flexible, this does NOT indicate the nails are "weaker". Instead, this is a temporary effect created by an increased moisture content of the nail plate. Nail coatings increase the moisture content of the plate by 10-15% and this can last up to 12-24 hours after coating removal; after which the moisture content returns to normal, as will the nail plate's normal level of rigidity.

When the nail surface is covered with dry looking white patches, this is usually due to improper removal, e.g. scraping or peeling nail coatings from the nail plate. Soaking the natural nail for even a few minutes in acetone or water will temporarily soften the surface making it temporarily more susceptible to damage from wooden or metal implements that pry, push or force the remaining residual nail coatings from the nail plate. Instead, a good rule to follow is, "Use the utmost care for 60 minutes after immersing natural nails in any liquid for more than 60 seconds." Other damage, e.g. onycholysis, is also usually caused by improper filing or removal techniques. For more information on avoiding nail damage see, "Don't Let This Happen to Your Clients", http://www.schoonscientific.com/educational-eblasts.html

Infections do occur, but they are relatively uncommon and can be easily avoided by practicing proper cleaning and disinfection. For more information see "Guidelines for Cleaning Manicuring Equipment", www.Probeauty.org/NMC

The facts are, when artificial enhancements or coatings are carefully and properly applied, maintained, and removed by a trained, skilled, and knowledgeable nail professional- they will not cause nail damage! The clear majority of damaged nail plates are caused by improper use- over filing and/or scraping the nail plate to remove products or by client nail abuse, e.g. picking or prying off nail coatings.

Myth 3: Vitamins and nutrients absorb into the nail to make them stronger and healthier. As described above, vitamins or nutrients can NOT be fed to the nail plate externally and in many countries, it is not legal to make such claims. Vitamins and/or nutrients only make nail plates stronger or healthier when they are ingested in foods and delivered to the nail via the blood stream. In the US and other places, it is against the law for a cosmetic to claim to provide nutritional benefits or value. Only foods can provide nutrition to the body, not cosmetics! To be clear, some nail oils use "vitamin E", but its function is NOT for nutritional purposes or strengthening. The proper cosmetic label name for Vitamin E is "tocopherol". Tocopherol or one of its related derivatives (e.g. tocopherol acetate) is used as an antioxidant to help protect the nail plate keratin from damage caused by environmental exposure (e.g. cleaners, hand washing, gardening). If no nutritional benefits are claimed, this is an appropriate cosmetic claim and there is strong science to support Vitamin E's antioxidant abilities. However, I am not aware of any evidence that demonstrates that any useful or significant amounts of "vitamins" can migrate from artificial nail coatings and absorb into the nail plate to provide benefits, so I recommend disregarding those claims until convincing evidence is provided.

Thank you and I hope you have enjoyed reading Face-to-Face with Doug Schoon, Volume II. If so, please encourage your nail friends to do the same and you'll be helping to raise the education level of the nail industry.

Index

Coming Fall, 2017

Face-to-Face with Doug Schoon

Volume III

Episodes 51-74

and

Special Topics

and

More!

Appendix Links

Free 3D "Anaglyph" Glasses Offer for Readers:

Rainbow Symphony, a specialty eye glass maker, has very kindly offered to send to all readers of this book one (1) free pair of 3D glasses which will allow viewing of the 3D images.

To get your free 3D glasses you must "exactly" follow the directions below:

Send a "Self-Addressed Stamped Envelope (SASE) with the proper return postage on the envelope to: Rainbow Symphony, Inc., 6860 Canby Ave. Suite 120, Reseda, CA, USA 91335. Mail the SASE inside the letter that you send to Rainbow Symphony. They will use your SASE to return your free glasses.

Make sure to specify the type of glasses needed as, "Paper Anaglyph Red/Cyan glasses". This is important to include.

If you do not include a "Self-addressed Stamped Envelope (SASE), with enough postage they won't have any way to send you the glasses, so this is very important. As of the printing of this book, US postage stamps are 0.49 cents.

Check your local post office for postage rates to your location if you are unsure. The glasses weigh no more than a standard letter with two sheets of paper included, so they are very light-weight.

This offer is good for anyone, anywhere in the world, but those living outside the United States MUST ensure the SASE has the proper amount of postage or the glasses cannot be sent to you.

For more information, see

https://www.rainbowsymphony.com/free-3d-glasses/

Note: Red/Cyan Anaglyph glasses may also be purchased on-line everywhere and found in many novelty shops, but the Left Lense must be "Red" and the Right Lense must be "Cyan" color.

Appendix Links cont.

Face-to-Face with Doug Schoon
www.FacetoFacewithDougSchoon.com

Nail Manufacturer's Council on Safety (NMC)
https://probeauty.org/nmc/

Guidelines for Controlling and Minimizing Inhalation Exposure to Nail Products
https://probeauty.org/docs/nmc/Inhalation.pdf

Nail Structure and Product Chemistry 2nd Edition
http://schoonscientific.com/purchase-books-dvd.html

Additional Reference Materials for Nail Professionals
http://dougschoon.com

Cosmetic Ingredient Information
http://www.cosmeticsinfo.org
http://personalcaretruth.com/

Dr. Joe Show
http://www.iheartradio.ca/cjad/shows/the-dr-joe-show-1.1761500

Acknowledgements

Technical Editor:

Holly L Schippers
FingerNailFixer®
http://fingernailfixer.com
http://youtube.com/fingernailfixer
http://facebook.com/fingernailfixer
http://instagram.com/fingernailfixer

Photographer:

Paul Rollins
http://paulrollinsphotography.com/

Back Cover Photograph:

Judy Landis-Storm

Made in United States
Orlando, FL
06 March 2025

59225629R00109

